A Garla

WAVENEY VAL[illegible] TALES

PREVIOUSLY PUBLISHED
BY THE AUTHOR

Larn Yarself Silly Suffolk
Tatterlegs For Tea

A Garland of
Waveney Valley Tales

DAVID WOODWARD

PENCIL SKETCHES BY
MARY BROWN

JOHN NICKALLS PUBLICATIONS

To Mike, Treeza, Jon, Aaron
and Martha

First published 2003

ISBN 1 904136 16 8

Published by John Nickalls Publications,
Oak Farm Bungalow, Sawyers Lane, Suton,
Wymondham, Norfolk NR18 9SH

Designed by Ashley Gray and Printed by Geo. R. Reeve Ltd,
9–11 Town Green, Wymondham, Norfolk NR18 0BD

Contents

Foreword

I HAVE KNOWN and admired David Woodward for over two decades, an endearing character always ready to share his talents as broadcaster, writer and performer. This collection of country tales reveals where much of his delightful raw material came from – and why so many others have revelled in his company.

A warm and witty colleague on *Press Gang* rounds with my local troubadours, David surely owes some of that compelling stage presence to his father's enduring reputation as a top-line entertainer with countless appearances in the Waveney Valley.

Born as the curtain began to close on Victorian times, Woodward Senior sang behind the silent screen and worked for 70 years with a firm of Beccles auctioneers. Ideal sources of inspiration as this volume of memories gathers pace.

David's childhood and the folk embellishing it give way to wartime episodes and early years working on farms at Gillingham and Aldeby. He forged lasting friendships and extended that affection towards an agricultural scene soon to be transformed by the march of mechanisation.

These yarns form a telling elegy for a rural era past, but they are rooted in real people and places rather than just soaked in sentimentality. A twinkling sense of humour, the traditional Woodward trademark, runs through the pages while Mary Brown's admirable illustrations give them extra lustre.

This is the Back'us Boy in his reflective prime, putting on a spread that wouldn't be out of place at the biggest harvest horkey. We tuck in gleefully – and ask for more.

Keith Skipper
Cromer, 2003

Acknowledgements

I HAVE MANY PEOPLE to thank for their help and encouragement in the preparation of this book, indeed I was most fortunate to once again have Mary Brown to illustrate the tales. We were contemporaries in Beccles, hence her sympathetic understanding of the characters and places she so vividly portrays. She is a joy to work with.

Thanks are due to Keith Skipper not only for his foreword but his encouragement to give an airing to some of the yarns on his *Radio Norfolk* Dinner Time programme and, more recently, with the Press Gang.

John Nickalls and Ashley Gray must be thanked for their friendly advice and expertise in the editing and publishing of the stories.

Peter Franzen, editor of the *Eastern Daily Press*, kindly gave permission to use a photograph taken at Hill Farm, Gillingham, and articles which had appeared in the *Eastern Daily Press* Country Scene pages.

Pippa Bastin, Managing Editor of Acorn Magazines, generously allowed us to reproduce two articles which appeared in the *Suffolk Journal*.

My son Michael, Treeza Sodah, Sandra Peary and Sami Gray have helped a lot in putting the script on computer disk for the publisher.

Thanks to Mr R T Bramley, Mrs M E Ashford-Hull and her son Michael, Mr and Mrs S Tredwell, Mrs Joan Wall and the *East Anglian Daily Times* for their help with photographs.

And finally to Jo Pigot and my wife Shirley for their patience and support.

David Woodward
Frostenden, 2003

Opposite: David Woodward and his wife Shirley.

JCW

SQUIBS WAS BORN in 1930 in Beccles, a small Suffolk market town of some six thousand souls on the banks of the River Waveney. But Norfolk hands drew him into this world for Dolly the midwife attending his birth cycled across the river marshes on the Gillingham dam and over the River Bridge into the town.

His tales go back beyond 1930, for his father, known affectionately by family and friends as JCW, lived to a great age and regaled him with yarns about Waveney Valley life at the end of the 19th century and into the 1900s.

As a toddler, JCW was taken by his father Mike to the churchyard, hoping to see Halley's comet when it came into view in 1910. At eventide they went into the churchyard that offered a clear view of the wide sky above the marshes of the river valley. A fellow shopkeeper, Caleb Chase the local newsagent, went with them. Canon Rowsell the rector had died earlier that day and Caleb's greeting when they met was, "Mike, we're a flock without a shepherd."

Alas, Squibs was never told if they had sight of the Comet.

Grandfather Mike was most fastidious about his food. Early morning he visited the local butcher or fishmonger to buy sausages, sweetbreads, kippers, bloaters, smoked haddock or whatever took his fancy for breakfast – eggs and bacon he took from his own grocery stock. In season, he loved fried sprats at teatime. The kitchen was his wife's domain, but she hated the thought of frying sprats, so Mike did this standing over the pan, one hand in his pocket, his children watching this event with some amusement.

Mike sent his sons to Beccles College, a school favoured in the area by local farmers and shopkeepers for their offspring.

Several years earlier, in 1895, Gilbert Jessop had been a pupil teacher at the college. Known as 'The Croucher' because of his stance at the wicket, he was in later years to become a famous cricketer for England. He joined Gloucestershire under the legendary W G Grace, who commented on Jessop's debut, "Well! We've found something this time!"

As to be expected Jessop produced heroic batting and bowling feats for the

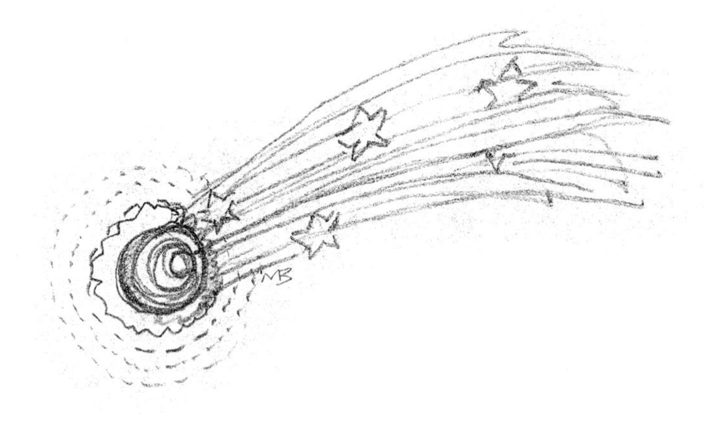

Halley's comet.

college team. JCW told Squibs that on one occasion Jessop hit the ball right out of the College meadow ground, which bordered the railway station. It flew over the railway sidings and station buildings, landing in a coal truck and was carried to Ipswich. W G Grace thanked Mr Hockey, the college headmaster, for occasionally allowing his young pupil teacher leave from school to play for Gloucestershire, but even the college headmaster would have found it hard to refuse W G Grace. And so Hockey helped Cricket!

JCW told Squibs how he met his mother in 1912 when there was a big fire at the local maltings near the railway station and College meadow. Olive, his future wife, was working as manageress at the station refreshment rooms. JCW and his father watched the fire crews at work in the early hours of the morning and, by 8am the blaze was under control, so they retired to the station diner for a cup of tea. And so Squibs' parents met as 18-year-olds, and fell in love. But they were not able to marry until the Great War was over some years later.

With his younger brother, JCW enlisted in the army, joining the 6th Suffolk Cyclists. The brothers were together for a time when they first joined the regiment. But the younger man was soon sent to France. He served in the trenches, returning only when he was wounded. JCW never went to France. Before embarkation the troops were subject to a more rigid medical and it was discovered he had a suspect heart. It probably saved his life and the heart kept on beating for a total of 95 years! Ironically, his younger brother died in his 60s of a heart condition.

JCW was stationed during the war at Orford, where his unit either slept in the castle or under canvas in the area. He made full use of his army bicycle, for he'd ride at weekends, or for longer leave, to see his sweetheart at the Beccles Station refreshment rooms. To his delight he found that she had struck up a friendship with his father. Mike took a great interest in his food and it was a bonus that his future daughter-in-law was an accomplished cook. They both shared an impish sense of humour. Several times a week Mike took his 'constitutional' down the Avenue, a tree-lined walk leading to the common and accessed via the station footbridge. Olive had a Pomeranian called Kim, which Mike whistled as he neared the station house. The dog whined to join him and to enjoy an extra walk and the little treat hidden in Mike's pocket. When Olive appeared with the dog he'd exclaim with mock surprise and a poker-faced expression "I s'pose I've got to take that damn flue-brush with me."

One afternoon Olive took her two younger sisters to visit Mike and his wife at home. He opened the door and exclaimed, "I expect next time you'll bring a whole charabanc load of your family." But he loved to have the three girls in his house and entertained them to a splendid tea.

A German Zeppelin.

The girls also provided teas and hospitality for wounded troops billeted and recovering in the town. There was a detachment of Lovat Scouts at one time. But it was a little wounded Cockney trooper who endeared himself to them. This was because of the reply he always gave when asked about his injury.

"The trouble was mam, I got 'it 'igh 'up in the 'ip."

While stationed at Orford Castle with the Suffolk Cyclists, JCW was involved in the action when a German Zeppelin was shot down in 1916 at Theberton, not many miles from their army camp at Orford. The events of that night became firmly entrenched in his mind and stayed with him to his dying day. He told Squibs how the German airmen knowing their craft was doomed decided to jump as it got near to the ground. Sadly they misjudged the distance and many fell to their deaths. One of JCW's duties was to collect the bodies of the dead airmen and place them in a makeshift mortuary in farm buildings in the village.

Later they were buried in Theberton churchyard. At a church parade on a Sunday soon after, a lady from the village placed a posy on the large grave with the words: 'In memory of some mother's sons'.

The Cerisians Are Coming!

THE GREAT WAR has been over some years. We are in the early 1920s, JCW, de-mobbed from the army, has returned to the Waveney Valley and has found himself a regular, if poorly paid, job. He often laughed with his son Squibs as he grew old saying, "I never had a well-paid job, but I never had to 'sign on' the dole either. For that I'm grateful."

JCW was looking to save up, find a home and marry his sweetheart. Alas his ambitions were forestalled when his father's grocery business was hit by the depression and he sold up to a more affluent local grocer and went back to work for him. Glad to lose the financial worries he'd gone through, he now took delight in secretly slipping gratis 'a little bit a cheese' to some of the poorer customers as they left with the weekly shopping order. At that time the rural labourer's wage had dropped to 25/6d a week.

The more-prosperous customers did not carry home their goods. No, for them it was only a question of taking their order book to the shop. A whistling errand boy delivered their provisions once or twice a week pushing a laden trade-bike to the door. Then he would ride back to the shop for more orders.

Squibs' grandparents moved from living over the shop into a humble cottage a few hundred yards away. As a young man, JCW's weekly wage helped towards the household expenses. So in his wish to marry and start a family he found sidelines to supplement his weekly wage. Fortunately his job as an auctioneer's clerk had reasonable and regular hours. Nine until five thirty was the norm apart from Friday sale-day or the extra farm and house content sales at Michaelmas. And the office where he worked, or the sale-yard, were only a few minutes walk from home.

JCW's other income came in complete contrast to his regular work and provided recreation that showed a profit. The silent films gained in popularity as folks sought pleasure and diversion after the horrors of the Great War and the hungry 'Twenties that followed. In their hometown, and in two market towns nearby, the cinema attracted a regular audience. In the larger City

Eventually their fame spread, even to Southwold!

cinemas musical interludes and accompaniment to the film was provided by a resident organist. The smaller venues could not go to such expense. But they could afford JCW whose fine light-baritone voice rang out from behind the silent screen accompanied by Mrs Esling on the piano. Songs were chosen to suit the narrative and style of the film. Through this work JCW increased his income and also got to know many people involved in the local town and village entertainment.

He was invited to join the 'Cerisians'. The group was so called because the ladies in the troop wore cerise frocks and the men silken shirts of the same colour. The Cerisians were well-known for their performances in the Waveney Valley and travelled one or two nights a week for what today would be described as a 'gig'. In those days a gig was a light, two-wheeled, one-horse carriage used by farmers and dealers travelling to the market and corn hall. Often they would carry home a gallon of whisky purchased at the local wine vaults for 3/6d (17.5p).

The Cerisians travelled in a waggonette, a four-wheeled, horse-drawn pleasure vehicle with side-facing seats. This was hired from 'Billy' who had one other cart – a horse-drawn hearse hired by local undertakers. Billy revelled in the contrast between his sober, silent daytime passengers and the Cerisian revellers jogging home from another successful entertainment. They were a motley crew. The other male singer was a tenor (and the groups booking and business manager) who rejoiced in the grand name of Newton Bolingbroke. Interestingly, it was with his family that Sir John Mills lodged for a time whilst a pupil at the local grammar school.

'Newty' was very, very, small in stature. So small that when he sang at local Masonic nights they seated him on a large over-mantle in the room. But he was an extremely popular member of the community. Everyone greeted Newty as he cycled around the town whistling or humming his latest aria. Years after his death his name and fame lived on in diverse ways. For instance Squibs used to play billiards and snooker at the local Men's Institute. There was a tall supporting pillar rising into the roof only a few feet from the yellow pocket on one table. It presented no problems for the players until the cue ball chanced to be near the cushion by the pillar. Then 'Newty' was called for. This was a specially adapted short sawn-off cue that did not buffet the pillar when a stroke was played. But it took skill and practice to play a potting shot with Newty. Sometimes, if a player found his score behind he'd not only look to snooker his opponent, he'd try to Newty him also! If he was successful a cheer went up from the onlookers.

JCW and Newty loved to reminisce. One of the tales became a legend in the Waveney Valley. The Cerisians had found fame for the quality of their performance around the towns and village halls in the area. They were hired for Masonic Nights, smoking concerts, dinners, parish suppers and harvest 'horkeys'. Eventually their fame spread, even to Southwold! Beccles, Bungay, Harleston, Loddon and nearby villages were the usual circuit. But to be invited to perform in Southwold! Surely they had reached the pinnacle. Two weeks before the performance a large advertising banner was hung across the High Street announcing: 'The Cerisians Are Coming!'

Pictures of the concert party were displayed in shop windows. The town awaited their show with anticipation and excitement. The box office had a sell out.

Alas, the Cerisians were not quite what Southwold had expected. The audience was 'surprised' by the content of the evening, some performers met polite clapping, but the more ribald jesters in the show were heard in stony silence. So different from the usual reception they received in the village halls. When the curtain rose after the interval the hall was half-empty. Many had sought early solace in The Crown or The Swan. But the Cerisians, stalwart troopers that they were, battled on bravely until the final curtain came down.

Subdued, they relaxed in the dressing room and made ready for the waggonette ride home. As was the custom, Newton Bolingbroke went to collect their fee from the concert organisers. He hurried back to join his fellow artistes with a saucy glint in his eye.

"How did you get on, Newty?" they asked anxiously.

"Hurry into the waggonette," he said, "they told me 'you've got your money, we've got ours, now get out of Southwold quick before they get you!'"

The troop crowded on to the waggonette. Billy 'gee'd the hoss up' and the Cerisians sped home from the Blythe to the comforting Waveney Valley.

Squibs and Aunt Marge

As a child in the 1930s, Squibs did not regard Aunt Marge as part of the family. She was someone who came to stay for her holidays at Christmas, Easter and for a week in mid-summer. She provided the lad with stories about life beyond his secluded Waveney Valley existence and a chance to see the sights of London.

Only when he grew into manhood did Squibs realise what an exceptional person Aunt Marge was. Most girls of her class, born into a humble Suffolk family, were destined to a life in domestic service, as retail shop girls or factory workers. Many were eventually to marry, raise a family and become hardworking housewives and mothers. This did not suit Aunt Marge as a career in London beckoned.

Held by her nephews in awe and wonderment, her arrival into the household was an event. Presents were distributed to everyone. A large box of 'Black Magic' chocolates was placed on the sideboard, handed around only as Aunt Marge decreed. Ginger marmalade graced the breakfast table when Aunt had coffee, not tea. She dressed more dramatically than the other female members of the family and the house permeated with an aroma from the powder, scent and eau-de-cologne she applied in abundance. You only had to open the front door to know that Aunt Marge had arrived!

All the family did their daily ablutions at the kitchen sink where, also, father shaved. On Saturday night, they bathed before the living-room fire in an old Victorian cream skimmer. The water was heated in a coal- and wood-fired copper in the kitchen. Oh – the blissful warmth in winter! This was not acceptable to Aunt Marge, who shared a bedroom with granny on her visits. Here she had an extensive 'toilette' daily in late afternoon. Hot water for this was readily carried to her room by Squibs in a large, copper-spouted jug with a hinged lid. This mission was worth an extra chocolate! Then, Aunt would change into more formal dress, even if she was to spend an evening at home.

Aunt Marge had a large Silver Fox fur; it hung on a peg in the hall. Squibs,

Aunt Marge had a large Silver Fox fur; it hung on a peg in the hall.

when very young, was terrified of the beady eyes in the fox's head and the snapping mouth that secured the fur around his Aunt's very ample bosom. A bosom so grand that when it heaved with the fur around it, the Silver Fox looked to have come to life! Squibs once dreamt that the fox bit Aunt Marge. The next day, he took the fur off of the peg and opened the mouth fastening to see if there was any of Aunt Marge inside. Luckily there wasn't! What a strange garment to wear, he thought. But it was the fashion and Aunt Marge liked to be up-to-date. Beneath her initially apparent tough exterior, she was mure-hearted. But she was set on being a career girl. To give her desires a chance she covered her sensitive soul with a cloak of determination. On some visits her paramour would accompany her.

Do not think that Aunt Marge was promiscuous. Quite the reverse. Years later, Squibs discovered that Teddie was her one and only constant lover. She may have had a few sweethearts, as we all do in youth, but he became her heart's delight. A businessman in the London drapery trade, religious scruples of the time, alas, stopped them from marrying. So they became lifelong, illicit, but faithful, lovers. Local people noticed, but she was, to outward appearances, unashamed and unmoved by the thoughtless and unkind criticism levelled at her by a few local hypocrites. True friends, thank goodness, accepted the situation with a wry smile.

Aunt Marge, unless you crossed her path unwisely, was good fun. The jocular one in the family, she was also well-off, by the standards of the day, enabling her to show her generous nature.

It is interesting how she came to leave the Waveney Valley and go into business in London. Her two younger brothers were sent to Beccles College. Aunt Marge, the only girl, had to glean as much knowledge as she was able at the local Dame school. She read a lot herself and had innate business skills. These she put to good use when she became an apprentice in the retail drapery trade at a large departmental store in Great Yarmouth.

As a young teenager she took lodgings in that town and, so, at an early age soon became self-reliant. Good at her work, she was spotted and recommended to Bourne & Hollingsworth, the large store in Oxford Street, London. The firm had family connections in Lowestoft. Well aware of the loyalty and hard work of Suffolk girls, they encouraged recruitment from the area. Comfortable and protected accommodation was provided for 'their' girls at Warwickshire House, a hostel in London. To there Aunt Marge went. She soon won rapid promotion within the firm and eventually became one of their head buyers, specialising in neckwear – hence the Silver Fox Fur! No mean achievement for a country lass today. In her age, it was outstanding.

As a buyer for the firm, she travelled to Edinburgh and Manchester in Britain, and to Europe, where she visited Paris, Brussels and Sans Sebastian in Spain. Whilst at Sans Sebastian the wholesaler she was buying from included her in a party of guests he took to the bullfight. She told Squibs of her disgust at the cruelty. It was even more horrendous and idiotic to her because the ceremony of torturing and killing bulls and maiming horses was linked to a religious Sunday festival. Eight bulls were to die that afternoon. Poor Aunt Marge – her tender heart for the sake of business acumen somehow managed to cope with the slaughter of four. Then she made her excuses and left. At the bottom of the steps leading from the bullring, she was violently sick. Years later, she told Squibs, "Don't you ever go to a bullfight!"

Aunt Marge continued as a buyer at Bourne & Hollingsworth until 1930 (the year Squibs was born). You can imagine, to reach such a position in the firm she had a very forceful personality. Somewhere along the line she crossed swords with one of the directors and it was decided they ought to part company. She recalled to Squibs how he snapped at her, "Get out of my office!" She did, and left, but negotiated on her departure from the firm a golden handshake of £1.00 per week for the rest of her life. A pittance today but a good deal for her then as it was more than half a labourer's wage. The director told her that if she lived to be seventy it would amount to a fortune. As an old lady in her nineties, Aunt Marge chuckled when she drew her weekly gratuity, by then increased to £1.30 due to inflation!

Probably due to the influence of Teddie, her boyfriend, who had connections in the drapery trade in the City, Aunt Marge now entered the wholesale side of the business. She took a managerial position with a firm by the name of Hitchcock Williams, whose workrooms were near St Paul's Cathedral.

Squibs remembers, soon after he had started school, going with the family, one Easter holiday, to spend a week at Aunt Marge's flat in London. Here he first saw and used a telephone and looked in wonder at the bathroom, with its tiles and gas geyser for hot water. It exploded into full flame, as if by magic, when you turned the tap on.

Two events on the trip stood out. One was the visit to the workshop where Aunt Marge's 'girls' were employed. The room was long and laid out with three rows of machines, with ladies working at them. It was noisy with the clutter of the workshop and the laughter and banter of the working 'girls'. They talked to each other loudly to be heard above the constant machine hum. Aunt Marge was a strict, but fair, manager and this made her popular.

"If they're happy, they work better and produce more. Encouragement is what they need," she said.

Squibs stood on a small, raised platform at the end of the room where the head machinist sat. He looked in wonder at Aunt Marge's 'girls'; some were in their sixties, but not all. One – Molly Du Pledge – was a real stunner. For some reason the boy could not take his eyes off her. He did not realise why! But Molly noticed Squibs looking at her and winked. She was pleasantly startled when the boy winked back. She beckoned him over and rewarded him with a packet of peanuts and a large Kit-Kat from her lunch box!

The climax of Squibs' first trip to London was a visit to the theatre in the

West End. They went to a show called *Going Greek*. Tom Walls, Richard Hearne (Mr Pastry) and Fred Emney were amongst the cast. Poor Squibs' heart sank when they took their seats. He was behind a large lady and no matter which way he moved he only had a partial view of half of the stage. Tears started to well up in his eyes. A passing usherette spotted his plight.

"I'll fetch you a cushion," she said.

"A cushion? That won't help much," the boy thought.

He need not have worried. When it came, the 'cushion' was a firm pouffe-type attachment that fitted into the seat. The lad was perched higher than any adult, giving him a full view of the stage. Squibs was enthralled by that first of many visits to the theatre. He was stage-struck that night and, from then on, he loved live entertainment, be it ballet, Shakespeare, drama, musicals or the circus. There was quite a bit of clowning in the show. One particular sketch the boy loved; it was one of those fill-in moments in a revue when the leading stars perform a cameo while the main stage is reset for the next spectacular. Fred Emney appears, riding a 'Stop Me and Buy One' ice-cream tricycle. His gigantic frame dwarfs the machine. He is joined by Richard Hearne, Tom Walls and a gorgeous chorus girl in tights. They decide to play Bridge but find that nobody has a pack of cards. Fred Emney opens a large tin of biscuits.

"Let's play Biscuit-Bridge!" he cries. Using his ice-cream box as a table top, they each receive a huge pile of biscuits, of every description:

TOM WALLS: "I lead one Huntley & Palmers' Breakfast."

RICHARD HEARNE: "I'll go three Rich Tea."

CHORUS GIRL: "I'll go two, my lovely Bourbons."

TOM WALLS: "Ooh! Ooh! I hoped you would!"

FRED EMNEY: "I'll Trumpet with a Cornet."

Curtain falls. Orchestra plays.

Squibs Joins the Back-Laners, 1940

FROM QUITE a tender age, Young Squibs was able to watch the activities of the back lane gang. Eventually the chance came for him to be fully admitted. His task to achieve this honourable status was to scrump 'two gret ole big apples' from a nearby orchard .What's more he had to do it all on his own without any assistance from the other boys.

The mission was accomplished one autumn Friday evening as he returned on an errand to get a 'loof' for his mum. He had waited until dusk to complete the task, telling his mum who expressed surprise at his late return, that he'd stayed for the last batch of bread. On the Saturday morning, when the gang met at half past nine, Squibs triumphantly showed his ill-gotten fruit to Len Hoster the gang leader. Len shook his hand and motioned the whole gang to form a large circle that filled the lane. Squibs took up a position in the middle of the circle.

There was Doc Fisher in steel-rimmed glasses, Bimsh Wall with auburn hair, Brother Woody, tall, and the second in command. Ted Lunn, who had a deep voice for a lad, stood beside his pal Buck Jones holding Rover the lane dog on a piece of plough line attached to his collar. A few other younger boys were also in the circle. Even Nello the lane champion was present. He was almost grown up and too old for boys' games, but now provided a paternal presence at special events. Nello was different in many ways from the others but held in high regard. His father played a violin.

"Not a fiddle," Nello proudly told the gang members, but a violin in the town's 'little light-symphony orchestra'.

But his son was broad, muscular and strong and he looked to have the potential to strum a double bass. Nello stood at twelve o'clock in the circle and Len at 6pm. Squibs handed them both an apple. They each took a bite, shook hands with Squibs passing him an apple back to hand to the all other boys in the circle for their bite. The occasion was solemn and carried out with a dignity that would have done credit to the Guards or a masonic night.

Young rustic ruffians they may have been at times but they were all very proud to be 'Back-Laners'.

The three Ripley girls stood watching a few yards away. They were followers of the gang and tolerated by the boys. As required they became Indian squaws, nurses, cooks or whatever female role was needed depending on the game of the day.

"Can't we just have a bit a core?" the oldest girl called.

"I hardly doubt there int a'goin to be no core," Bimsh called back.

But Bimsh had a few tiny Beauty of Bath apples in his pocket from a tree in his uncle's garden. An early eater they had become a bit 'clung' now. But even in their shrivelled state he knew his apples were riper and sweeter than the Dr Harvey's, young Squibs had scrumped. Bimsh had quite a way with the girls.

"Try these," he said and 'copped' the girls one each. They grinned back at him as they sank their teeth into the wizened, but sweet, harvest-time apples.

Soon after Squibs' initiation, three more boys joined the gang. The leader was anxious to recruit some extras into the ranks as soon as possible and with good reason. For word had got around through the gang's intelligence network the Ellough Roadsters and the Castle Hillites were aiming to rival the Back-Laners' supremacy in the town.

The rival gang was made up from youngsters growing up on a recently-built council housing estate on the fringe of town. Their members were now bent on becoming the town's top gang. Until now, Len Hoster and the Back-Laners were the undisputed leading gang. No matter what the challenge, Bibby-hole marbles, Titta-ma-torta riding, Pop Gun Making, Conkers, Wooden Sword Fighting, Pea Shooters, Hop rolling, Honky Donk Spark Flying and even Hop Scotch. The Back-Laners were tops. The site of the lane was ideal. It was wide with a high hedge and the orchard and allotments beyond. An iron-foundry, maltings and three builders' yards nearby gave interest to the region. There was always something happening. A shummaker, an old boy who stuffed birds, and a fortune-teller all added to the charm and fascination of the area. The town common, an ideal haunt for gang adventures in holiday time, was only ten minutes' walk away. Small wonder that boys from other areas of the town were pleased to be enrolled if given the opportunity. This would happen when they were able to offer some special contribution. Pop Laws, who's father owned a mineral-water factory, was recruited for obvious reasons. Chalky White and Stingy Weavers lived on the

Grange – far too posh a part to have a local gang. But they were able to bribe their way in as Back-Laners. Chalky White did this with conkers from horse-chestnut trees near his home. Stingy Weavers had access to two massive oak trees laden with acorns in the autumn. These he supplied as ammunition for the gang's pop-guns made from hollowed elder branches.

It was considered you were one of the élite to become a Back-Laner.

Young Squibs was 'wholly proud' when he became a fully-fledged member.

Wooden Sword Fighting.

Send For Nello

THE BACK-LANERS were worried. Their intelligence network had picked up, from a reliable source, that an attack from the 'Castle Hillites' and the 'Ellough Roadsters' was being planned.

Three of the more affluent families in the road employed a maid. Two of the girls lived-in but one – Hetty – walked every day from Ellough Road to help in Squibs' household. This was one of the more humble cottages in the terrace. For them to have a maid, therefore, was most unusual. But, in later life, he found out this was possible for two reasons. His parents looked after Granny, his father's mother. She was the widow of a popular former grocer in the town and had financial help from local organisations. Coupled with this, further aid came from Aunt Marge, who had found fame and fortune in London.

Hetty had heard of the activities of the rival gang and mentioned it to Squibs' mum as they were finishing the Friday bake. Squibs was just home from school and sat in the kitchen eating one of mum's 'Tatterlegs' fresh from the oven. There was a small elm kitchen chair tucked in a cosy corner out of the way of the cooking but it gave the occupant full view and hearing of everything going on.

Hetty, by the sink, said to his mum, "We love livin' in them there new Council Housen; there's even a bath in the kitchen you can fill from the boiler. Father wholly love a soak in that when he come home from trawling. There's so many families and boys growin' up around; the trouble is those boys have got together in two large gangs, and they aim to be top in the town. A friend told us their plan is to come marauding to other parts. She said they'll be a'comin' down your back lane this weekend on what they call a 'charge'!"

Squibs' ears pricked up. He finished the 'Tatterleg' and went down the back garden into the lane. There were always one or two lads about after school and, luckily, Len Hoster, the leader, was there. Squibs told him what he had just heard.

"Well done bor!" said Len. "I 'int surprised but now we'll be ready for them."

Len knew that the Ellough Roadsters would far outnumber the Back-Laners. If they charged through another gang's territory, their aim was humiliation. They did not seek to cause injury but would not be averse to capturing bounty in the form of go-carts, catapults, hoops or pop-guns. Stocks of apples, conkers and acorns were likewise fair game. High School hats, compulsorily worn by some boys, would be flung over the hedge or trodden in to the mud. If hand-to-hand fighting did take place, the vanquished victim was rolled on the ground and held for a few moments. No serious injury was likely to occur but the intensity of feeling between the rivals was great. It was boyish fun, and bravado, taken to the then bounds of propriety.

"If they are coming this weekend," said Len, "it will be Saturday morning. Most of them will be in the tuppenies at the 'Fleapit' in the afternoon. It's getting dark by the time they get home."

Len did not even bother to spell out the fact that even the Ellough Roadsters would not violate the Sabbath on such an escapade. There would have been no point, a good tidy few of them would be at Sunday School or church. And the Back-Laners had a number of church choristers in their midst. In those days the lane was often deserted on a Sunday.

Warning messages were quickly got to all the gang members. A coded message was used to advise everyone to meet in the lane. Part of a ditty used in play was spoken from member to member:

"One, two, three,
Mother caught a flea.
Put it in the teapot,
Made a cuppa tea."

As they sat at tea that night, young Squibs burbled out the code to his older brother.

"Don't talk such nonsense at the meal table!" said dad. Granny gave the little puttering cough she used to signal disapproval. No matter; the message got through.

Early that evening, the gang met to plan their campaign. A lookout was to be stationed at the far end of the allotments. He was to climb a tall beech tree to give himself an early sight of the raiding gang approaching. The warning signal was a loud cock-crow. Skippy Reynolds had a perfect 'cock-a-doodle-do' call and so was sent to be the scout in no-mans-land. Under Len's direction, lengths of plough-line were tied in the lane hedge every ten yards or

Nello was their Back-Lane Beowulf.

so. They were laid loosely on the ground so as not to impede the passage of grown-ups and various tradesmen going about their lawful business in the lane. The plan was as the Ellough Roadsters made their tribal charge the ropes would be pulled tight by Back-Laners, secreted behind their garden gates. The rival gang would stumble on the ropes. Then water pistols would be used to drench the victims. Buckets of water were placed in readiness to quickly recharge the pistols. The weather was chilly enough to make them an effective deterrent. At ten o'clock on the Saturday morning the Back-Laners were ready, like troops waiting to go over the top.

At ten thirty-seven precisely (for Len kept battle records), the cock-crow from Skippy drifted across the allotments. Len gave a less-authentic call himself to make sure everyone was alerted. Cunningly, the Ellough Roadsters surged from two fronts. One section came into the middle of the lane, through the allotment gates. The main body charged from the bottom entrance. They had walked quietly along a passageway through the centre of an iron foundry at the end of the lane. Len and Doc Fisher stood at the top of the lane taunting the attackers with cries of, 'Come and get us!' There were only four more boys with them and they looked easy prey. The rival gang fell into the trap just as Len had planned. They rushed full pelt up the lane and ran into the trip ropes. The water sprinkling added to their discomfort and they soon became a damp and dejected bunch.

"Surrender?" cried Len to Chubby, their leader.

"You wait!" cried Chubby.

Alas, the Back-Laners had forgotten that the Castle Hillites had yet to appear. They had quietly walked in two's and three's up the front road. Grouping at the top, they formed in ranks and charged from the other direction of the lane. Mock wooden-sword fights now took place and were going against the 'Laners. Several found themselves bound in the plough-line trips. It looked as though, in spite of their preparation, the Back-Laners would be vanquished.

But Len had one more trump card up his sleeve.

"Send for Nello!" he cried, and his call was taken up by his fellows.

"Send for Nello…. Send for Nello…" echoed across the lane. The Ellough Roadsters and their allies looked startled and apprehensive. Most of them had heard of this former gang-champion who they incorrectly thought had left the area. But Nello, now almost grown up, was still there in a crisis. He burst into the land, carrying a galvanised metal dustbin lid as a shield, whilst whirling a thick piece of knotted rope above the heads of the rival gang. Fearful as he looked, it was his yelling that struck terror, coupled with the clattering of the dustbin lid. His arrival was unexpected and spurred Len's boys to regroup and renew battle. Nello was their Back-Lane Beowulf. No dragon his adversary, his mission was to preserve the honour and pride of their locale. The Ellough Roadsters and the Castle Hillites took fright and ran!

Never again was the Back-Laners territory violated. When the next harvest holidays came, the gangs met on the Common as opponents in football and cricket matches.

And Nello was the umpire!

Squibs and Miss Jefferson, 1938

ALONG THE HALLWAY of the cottage was a row of pegs where the family's coats and hats hung. At the end of the hall, and at the bottom of the stairs, was a windowsill, now utilised as a shelf. On it were placed two clothes brushes and a hairbrush, with a comb nestling in the bristles. Beside this was a small box containing a selection of hair- and hat-pins. The sill was quite wide and big enough to also hold a small pile of various gloves and scarves. Granny often put her glasses case on it when she descended the stairs, around midday, for dinner, then forgot it until she wanted to change her glasses to read the *Radio Times* after tea. A panic search would then ensue; on warm, summer days it was quickly found, but in bitter wintry weather it would be buried under a pile of gloves and scarves. The windowsill was still of great use but the window, a former source of dawn's eastern light and morning sun, had gone. Gone long before the arrival of Squibs' granddad and family into the road. The nextdoor neighbour's house had been built close alongside. And so, a one-time pair of double-dwellers, known rather grandly as 'Belgrove Villas', became part of a row of terraced houses.

No careful planning restrictions in those days! Most of the housing was developed by speculative landlords, to let. More houses, more rent, no worry if we block a few windows out in the process! However, never once did Squibs hear anyone question why the neighbouring house had been built in such a way.

In the early 1930s, the house was occupied and owned by Mr & Mrs Lee and Miss Lee, a maiden sister they called 'Doogie'. No one else was granted the doubtful privilege of addressing Miss Lee so. The senior one of the three, her principal role was now dusting furniture, making the tea and preparing knitted or crocheted tea cosies. These were gifted to friends, or sold at church fêtes and bazaars.

Mr Lee was a retired businessman. He wore a suit and a clean, stiff, white collar every day; but, in the house, he removed his jacket for a comfortable,

Granny often put her glasses case on it when she descended the stairs, around midday, for dinner,

finely-knitted cardigan. An authority on clocks and watches, he had a small collection in the front room. He did amateur, but reliable, repairs for friends and family. He was a round little man, always unruffled, and the household was a scene of serene domesticity. His wife played her part in this. She was a retired schoolteacher who helped Squibs a lot when he started at the Infants' School. He talked to 'Missa' Lee about his schoolwork. A dedicated teacher, she welcomed the fact that next door were young boys she could help. But Miss Lee did more than just help Squibs; at a tender age she awakened in the boy a love of listening to, and telling, stories. She made learning fun, giving him a series called *My Language Books*. Originally published in America, in 1929, they contained stories, poems and exercises the boy loved to do.

The family had connections overseas. Mr and Miss Lee championed the course of the British & Foreign Bible Society. They were regular attendants at the Parish Church at least twice every Sunday. But they were not what Squibs' mum called 'Bible Thumpers'. They lived by example.

Eventually they benefited from a legacy and moved to a grander house in the Station Road. It was a good move, the boy thought, as they were still near enough for him to be able to visit on his own. The new house had a long garden and a small orchard, which Squibs passed through on his way to see them. He would do shopping errands in return for school tuition, biscuits and windfalls. Miss Lee had a tin with a ready supply of Petit Beurre, Osborne and Rich Tea biscuits. In very hot weather, she drank China Tea, with a lemon slice. What bewildered the boy was that she did not add sugar. But, luckily, he was allowed three lumps in his. And chance time an extra one to eat. There were silver tongs on the tray to pick them up.

Mr Lee would appear and quietly join the tea party. He showed the boy his special weather barometer. It was in the form of a model house, with a verandah. A figure of a maiden came out of one door, if fine and calm weather was indicated. When wind and rain was likely, she retreated indoors and a male figure appeared from the other door. This was a source of wonder and enchantment to all children visiting the household, and there were quite a few as Mrs Lee also taught at the local Sunday School.

The departure of the Lees from next door heralded the arrival of Miss Jefferson as the new neighbour. What a change she was! An eccentric spinster, she lived alone; her only company being an enormous black cat. Miss Jefferson came from a village far afield, near Ipswich. A mystic, she told fortunes and practiced palmistry, entertaining 'paying clients', as she called them, in her front room.

Miss Jefferson was one of the few people in the road using their front room regularly. Front rooms were usually reserved for Christmas, possibly piano practice, giving the Rector a cup of tea, weddings – and funerals when the body was kept there for a few days prior to the funeral and respect was paid to the deceased.

Miss Jefferson told people's fortunes by looking into the palm of their hand and measuring, what she called, the lifeline and the loveline. But she practiced other mystic operations. She used an inkpad to take thumbprints of her clients; these were then pressed on to fine white paper. Then, in the brightest light she could achieve, and by using a fine mapping pen, she would trace out figures and names she was convinced she saw in the thumbprint.

During the winter, there was a steady flow of callers and the fee was a florin (20p today!). Nobody in Squibs' family had any wish to visit Miss Jefferson for occult advice. Uncle Claud, on holiday in the Waveney Valley, once jokingly wondered if she might help with his football coupons, or give him a Derby winner! He never ventured to ask. Then, one year in early summer, Uncle Tom and Aunt Lil made one of their infrequent visits. They came from Sussex where Uncle Tom was a Horticultural Adviser. He smoked a pipe and wore heavy tweeds. When he discovered Squibs loved the countryside and being on farms, he presented him with his twelve volumes of *A Standard Cyclopaedia of Modern Agriculture*, published in 1912. They are still on Squibs' bookshelves and contain splendid plates and drawings. Aunt Lil soon heard about Miss Jefferson, the new neighbour, and, being one of those people anxious about the future, decided on a visit to the next door neighbour's front room for a spot of palmistry. You can imagine the family were curiously awaiting her return and hoping to share the results. Aunt Lil was gone some time and Squibs' mum decided to stroll down the road after supper. Upon her return, everyone asked, "Any sign of Aunt Lil?"

"Oh, I looked in the window," she said. "Lil is laying across the table, flat on her back with her legs and arms in the air! Miss Jefferson is in flowing robes, the cat is on her shoulder and she's dancing round the room and chanting!"

But it must have done Aunt Lil good. She came home very composed, slept like a log and ate a huge breakfast the next morning!

It was through Miss Jefferson's cat that Squibs got quite friendly with her. Often, the cat would remain in the small garden or sit in a large elderberry tree, which had been allowed to grow rampant by the back door. Elderberry aroma was said to keep the flies away in summer. As all cats must at times, it would sally forth on hunting expeditions down the back lane and on the nearby allotments. This did not worry Miss Jefferson, as long as it returned for supper at eight o'clock. It was summoned by its owner calling it, using a peculiar hissing sound she reverberated through her lips and false teeth. She managed to achieve an alternating and strong volume to the hiss. It was easily heard next door when she reached full crescendo, as it was always about the time the family took their cocoa . The conversation often went like this.

"Time to put the milk on for the cocoa?"

"Oh! Has Miss Jefferson hissed the cat yet?"

Now and again the cat hissing did not work. It was then that Squibs was summoned by Miss Jefferson to go down the lane in search of the foraging feline. The boy carried a few little treats, given him by Miss Jefferson, to lure the cat home.

In return for these missions of mercy, Squibs was rewarded by a trip to Lowestoft during the harvest holidays in August. For a few weeks, the seafront was thronged by crowds of holidaymakers and day-trippers. Whilst the corn was being safely gathered in on the farms, others, many from the Midlands and the North, were enjoying the beach and seaside. And Miss Jefferson had her own Fortune Telling Harvest. She became 'Madam Pauline' on the seafront promenade. Dressed in flowing robes, and secluded in an ornate tent, she plied her craft for the excitement and anticipation of those holidaymakers who hoped to be foretold a life of riches and fame ahead.

Next to 'Madam Pauline's' stall was an ageing, retired jockey, dressed in his brightly-coloured riding silks, complete with whip. His enterprise was to weigh customers, mostly young mothers, on an authentic set of jockey scales. He kept up a jovial, disarming banter in the process. Then, when a lass was weighed in, he had no problem persuading her to have a snap taken standing beside him, by a photographer who plied his trade along the promenade. It was a singular memento to take home from holiday.

The highlight of a trip to the seaside with Miss Jefferson was a visit to the Fish & Chip Emporium before they caught the train home. On one day, the Fortune Telling trade had been brisk and Squibs was rewarded with the masterest piece of fried cod he had ever seen, surrounded by golden chips. He smothered it, to Miss Jefferson's amusement, in tomato ketchup, washing the feast down with lemonade. They caught the 6.19pm home and Squibs was handed over to his mum at the front garden gate with the words, "He won't want much tea!"

Old Jessie

"DO YOU RUN down to Billy Downs and git a fi stone a' mixed corn for the ole hens – we're right out. Been so busy over Christmas I'd forgot," said JCW to his nine-year-old son. The boy Tom looked disconsolate. It was ten minutes before five o'clock and children's hour would soon be on the wireless. Toy-town was on tonight – one of his favourite programmes. And what was worse it was bitterly cold outside and the freezing fog that had been threatening all day descended as dusk approached. As always, in frosty weather, the huge coal fire glowed red in the grate. Grandma, in the chair against it, was softening the butter to spread on the toast she would soon be making. The boy loved to hold the telescopic toasting fork for her that was kept on a hook by the overmantle. It was New Year's Eve in 1938.

"Hurry Tom – or Bill will be closed," urged his father. The voice was sterner this time and by its tone his son knew he would be ill-advised not to obey. Grandma had weighed up the situation also. She uttered not a word but gazed at the boy and gently jerked her head towards the back door that Tom would leave by. As he passed her she gently palmed two shining new pennies into his hand. She always kept a stock of bright new-minted coins in one compartment of her purse. They, coupled with a large tin of humbugs, helped to endear her to her grandchildren. So Tom set off on his dad's errand with more joy in his heart than when the request was first made. His father, a kind but strict parent, had promised, if the boy behaved himself, he would be allowed to see the New Year in for the first time ever. Missing Toy Town would be a small price to pay if it ensured he stayed up until after midnight.

A bottle of raisin cordial was in the sideboard and he with his elder brother and sister would use this to toast in the New Year. The grown-ups had sherry but the children would be allowed to drink their cordial from the same glasses. Tom would easily pretend he was downing a glass of sherry. The cordial was sherry colour. A tactful purchase by mother who knew how to toady to her children's imagination.

But it was Grandma's two pennies that made the once supposedly dismal errand into a joyous mission. One penny would buy two of Dusty's halfpenny saffron buns from his bake-house near the corn chandlers. The other penny would go into the little savings bag the boy kept in his sock drawer. Made by Grandma from an odd scrap of deep-red velvet material, it closed by a small red-leather lace drawstring. It already held three silver threepenny bits from Christmas presents, four farthings and, treasure of treasures, a florin remaining from the last quarterly choirboys' payday.

The bag also held a small metal 'put and take' spinning top and four prize glass alleys he did not want mixed with the mundane clay marbles kept in another box.

Tom sped quickly on his way but the journey home would perforce be slower. A half stone of mixed corn was a big enough load for a nine-year-old to carry, even a stocky lad like Tom. But dad had come up with a crafty solution. His son carried the feed for the hens in two large old linen cashier's money bags acquired from a local bank (Father and the manager of the bank both sang in the church choir). A length of broad soft cord tied the bags together. When full the chandler placed them across the boy's shoulders and he would carry them home like a pack-mule. And his hands would be free for the planned purchase of saffron buns.

"Mind you don't slip on the ice!" cried dad as his son sped down the backyard on his errand.

There were two different routes to the corn chandlers. One well lit by street lamps which eventually took you past all the shops along a busy road towards Billy Downs' corn and feed business. But another quicker way took a shortcut through what everyone called the Folly. The problem was that the Folly, a narrow footpath lane, was not properly lit by street-lamps. A lamp at both ends of the lane shone a glow for a distance into the pathway. But there was a dark and murky section of some twenty yards in the middle. Because of this Tom would normally have gone a much-preferred longer journey past all the shops. The boy was aware that his earlier reluctance to go immediately at his father's request meant he had only five minutes before the shops closed. If he ran quickly through the lane he need only be in the dark for less than five seconds. He decided to take the short cut on the outward journey and return laden with the hen food by the longer route past all the bright shop windows. With beating heart he reached the Folly and sped into the darkness. The freezing fog had set low only a few feet above the ground. In the sky, snow clouds sped across the moon but at times there was more than a hint of moonlight. Alas, just as he reached the unlit part of the Folly, a thick cloud

Jessie was cooking a sausage in a small metal pan.

veiled the moon and huge flakes started to fall blowing cold into his hot face. Tom was scared but the realisation he would soon be clear of the darkness spurred him on. But suddenly fear turned to terror. For the child ran straight into the arms of Old Jessie Rymer, who stood unseen in the middle of the track. In his excitement and wish to reach the shop and bakehouse before they closed he had completely forgotten that old Jessie had taken up her usual winter residence in the tall hedge on the east side of the Folly. Old Jessie's mode of life was such that children avoided her. At least they did on their own. Sometimes a small gang of boys might act as her tormentor throwing snowballs and insults to the poor soul. But mainly because of her appearance and the fact she never spoke, Tom and his pals feared her.

Old Jessie was a victim of the Great War. Coming from a genteel middle-class background she was the daughter of a solicitor and had married a clergyman's son. He had been an officer in the Suffolk regiment in the Great War and had survived trench warfare returning to marry his sweetheart. 'My Jess' he lovingly called her. Alas their idyllic life together was tragically cut short. Having gone through the war and the terrors of the trenches, Jessie's husband, weakened from his wartime experiences, succumbed to the outbreak of influenza that swept across Europe in 1919. Within two days he was dead and Jessie heartbroken. Not able to cope with life in their country cottage she became a wanderer and recluse. Now, some nineteen years later, her life-style was eccentric but followed a set routine. All through the spring, summer and autumn she lived in the surrounding villages. She had a rotation of farms, large country houses and rectories she visited. Never staying more than a month in the same area she moved from village to village. Most of the local farmers and clergymen were aware of Jessie's history. She posed no threat to anyone and so a blind eye was turned if Jessie was discovered sleeping in a local barn. When she moved on everything would be left as she found it. In many cases a certain amount of help was given her. She had no conversation with anyone but was content to receive gifts with a thank you nod. Often a mug of tea, a bowl of soup or hunks of bread and cheese would be handed to her across the back'us door. She always tried to find a farm where a few dairy cows were kept, which most did in those days. Then a glass of warm milk, straight from the cow, was eagerly gulped down by Jessie. In return she would potter about weeding or hoeing in the kitchen garden. She may have opted out of normal life but had not given up on her will to live and always tried to give something in return for the small gifts she received.

Each winter in early December she made her way into town and took up residence in the hedge of the Folly. It was tall and thick with a huge beech tree growing on the farther side. Against the tree Jessie constructed her winter bivouac. Her choice of site was a good one. The Folly lane was narrow, only a yard or so wide and the other side was bordered by a tall brick maltings wall. Along this, vents from the malting process issued a steady flow of steam. Even on this bitter New Year's Eve it provided shelter and raised the ambient temperature a few degrees. But on this particular night it enhanced the eeriness around Jessie's abode. For the steam only mingled and thickened the low icy mist forming in the darkness. Jessie was a sturdy lady and the thick long skirt, warm woolly hat and long overcoat she wore through the winter plus a wide coomb sack apron, tied round an area that might have been her waist, only added to her considerable girth. Young Tom ran into her wallop and bounced back almost two feet. Even in the dim light Jessie was aware of the extreme fear in the boy's eyes.

It was years since she had spoken to anyone. But she did now to Tom.

"Steady, lad," she said, her words came not in sentences for she had lost the art of conversation.

"Coming so fast: not see you: silly to run: icy track: slippery."

But her voice was kind gentle and soothing. Tom could feel his fear receding enough for him to blurt out: "Got to get some mixed corn for father's ole hins. Shop will soon shut. Then there will be trouble. And 'ont see the New Year in."

"Go on sonny," said Jessie, "be careful."

It was the first time she had had a conversation with anyone for years. The boy disappeared on his errand and was soon at the chandlers and collecting the mixed corn. It was yoked across his shoulders and he walked slowly up the road and collected his two halfpenny saffron buns from Dusty's bakehouse. Then he did something that surprised himself. He could not stop thinking of poor Old Jessie and the soft gentle tone in her voice. His tender heart was overwhelmed not by fear of her but a feeling of compassion.

"Blas that must be whooly cold and lonely for her in that old shack – whatever must she do for wittles?" he wondered. On an impulse he decided to go back home again via the Folly and share his saffron buns with the poor old lady. When he reached Jessie's bivouac she had gone back in the shelter. He was surprised to find her placidly sitting on a huge chaff sack that was stuffed with straw. She was cooking a sausage in a small metal pan like the troops used in the trenches. The heat, he was amazed to see, was supplied from two candles. But the sausages were sizzling in the pan. Suspended on a line of binder twine across the top of her shack was a huge bunch of dried herbs and lavender. These coupled with the aroma of slowly cooking sausages helped to disguise and improve the smell that surrounded poor Jessie. For most of the year around the farms she was able to keep herself reasonably clean washing in marsh dykes or pulks. Sometimes a friendly farmer would let her have a bucket of hot water from his dairy. Although Tom thought of her as old she was in early middle age and quite active. In the warmer weather she looked younger. But in the winter Jessie seemed to age five years for every layer of garments she clad herself in. And she wore as many as possible until the daffodils bloomed and she had her spring clean on her return to the country farms along the Waveney Valley.

The boy gingerly proffered Jessie one of his saffron buns at the same time pulling back the sacking drawn across the shack entrance. The recluse motioned to a small stool for the boy to sit. Tom cast his mixed corn burthen to the ground and took his seat on the stool. Slowly they each ate a saffron bun in silence. Then Jessie spoke, again slowly and still not forming sentences. It was like someone starting to walk again after a long spell of sickness.

"Good buns – boy," she said. "Mustn't be long – mum – worry?"

"Yis," said Tom and he left Jessie's shack without another word. They smiled at each other, their faces just discernible in the flickering candlelight, and Tom was gone.

In the excitement of seeing the New Year in Tom forgot all about his adventure until about five minutes past midnight when all the family walked to the top of the road and listened to the church bells ringing in the New Year.

"Strange!" Tom thought you could see the church bell tower above the rooftops in the now starlit sky. But the sound appeared not to be emanating from that direction. It wafted through the frozen air, carried on the northeast wind it bounced against the high brick maltings building and dissolved over the Folly and Old Jessie's bivouac. So the boy's thoughts turned again to the lady. He thought of her lonely and cold. He'd talk to his mum about her thinking: "Best not mention it to anyone else".

About three days later he confided with his mother and told her the full story about his meeting with Jessie in the Folly. How he had shared the saffron buns with her and that she, to his surprise, had been kind and gentle to him and not like all his chums had thought. His mum listened with amusement and pleasure. She gave Tom a shortcake to give her each time he was going through the Folly. He took the short cut when he went back to school after the Christmas and New Year holidays. Because of this he was able to spend five minutes longer over breakfast. He and Jessie would chat for a minute or two each morning. She always asked what he was doing at school that day and if he had done his homework.

The weeks passed and it was time for Jessie to move back into the countryside and have her spring clean. One morning in late March Tom found her packing all her chattels into an old pram that she used to carry her belongings. The packing was almost complete and Jessie joined him and they walked together along the Folly path. Coming to a minor road junction Tom had to go right for his school and Jessie left along a lane that led to the open countryside and her first farm visit.

"Good bye, boy," she said, "see you next winter?"

She did not hug him, but for the first time since her sweetheart had died she touched another human being. For she gently gripped Tom's shoulder as they parted.

A few weeks later it was market day in the town. A group of farmers were having their usual Friday mardle concerning the week's events as they gathered on the steps of the corn-hall entrance at the end of the day. Through the winter these meetings took place around a huge log fire in the adjacent King's Head hotel. Now in the softer aired spring weather they gathered in small groups outside.

"Old Jessie turned up again as usual last week," said one. "But do you know bor she've whooly changed, she come up to the back-door this time and asked if she might sleep in the barn a few nights. Missus made her a cup a tea and give her a jug a milk. And she reckon old Jessie stayed and chatted a few minutes. Then she went and put the hoe through the broad beans!"

A similar procedure happened wherever Jessie went that year. By harvest time she was chatting quite freely in each village she went to.

Life was never joyous for her again, but a small boy's kindness had made it tolerable.

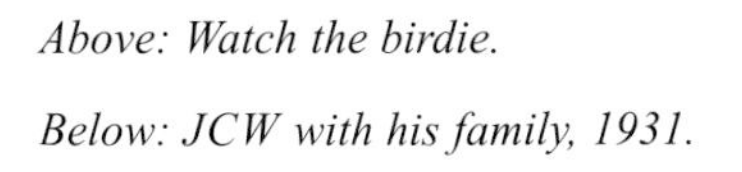

Above: Watch the birdie.

Above right: How far to the boundary?

Below: JCW with his family, 1931.

Above: Gillingham Dam, 1926.

Below left: Aunt Marge, aged 16 years. *Below right: In their Easter Bonnets, 1926.*

February

IT WAS CHILLY mid-February in 1936. Squibs was suffering from what his dad described as a severe feverish cold. It was made worse because he developed 'Pink Eye' requiring drops of 'healing stuff' thrice daily. His eyelids felt like sandpaper when he closed them, the poor little ole' chap was certainly under the weather. The family 'panel' doctor, paid for by the 'Oddfellows', had looked in twice to see him.

"Keep him warm! Make him drink all you can!" he said. "He needs to find something to take his mind off it."

How? His mum pondered. The boys bedroom was small and at the rear of the cottage, the only outlook was on to the next-door neighbour's high wall. If you stretched your head out of the tiny casement window it was possible to get a glimpse of the fruit trees on nearby allotments, or the tall hedge that grew along the back lane. Not much to interest a young mind recovering from the effects of high fever. Then his mum had one of her brilliant ideas. Wrapped cosily in dad's furry, blue and grey dressing gown, he walked with faltering steps along the short landing to lie on his parents' bed in the front bedroom. With the bed pushed nearer to the large sash window, the net curtains removed and the others drawn back, he had an uninterrupted vision of all the days' proceedings in the road. And, although it was only a little side street in a small, market town in Suffolk in the Waveney Valley, there was much for the boy to observe.

Across the road was the old, former Cottage Hospital, now converted to three separate dwellings. In one wing lived the manager of the local Labour Exchange. His office was a long, narrow, green, wooden hut which stood in the garden beside the house. He was able to walk straight out of the back door and into his office. Every morning, from about nine o'clock, the unfortunates 'on the dole' – and there were many in the hungry 'thirties – would gather to 'sign on'. Squibs did not, in the early years of his life, realise that 'the unemployed', as they were known in the town, represented a few of the country's broken hopes and dreams of thousands who had returned from the Great War to a 'land fit for heroes'. Memories of those men 'signing on'

There was much for the boy to observe.

stayed with him all his life. At the moment, on this chilly February morning, they were but a welcome diversion from the boredom of sickness. The lad always chatted to everyone he met in the road and had got to know two regular clients at the Exchange in particular.

He tapped on the window to one. Badly deformed, he was bent over and walked with a limp. In a strange way he somehow supported himself by placing one hand on his knee, the trouser on this leg heavily patched to prevent wear from the continuous pressure. But although practically doubled in half, he speedily proceeded along the pavement to his daily destination. He never wore an overcoat, even in cold weather. His loose-fitting, elbow-patched, tweed jacket, obtained at a local jumble sale, was worn winter and summer alike. But as it turned colder he added a series of woollies beneath his jacket. As was the custom in those days, from October to May he would also have worn a thick woollen vest and long pantaloons. A cloth cap, set at an angle, covered his head and although his hair was dark, he had bright-blue, watery eyes, which gazed happily out from his weatherbeaten face on to the world. Around his neck he wore a faded red and white spotted 'kerchief'. And from his breast pocket he frequently produced another one to wipe away the continuous flood of moisture from one eye. To lessen the effect of his stooped gait, he turned his head, slightly cocked upwards, to one side all the time. He looked like a robin and, in the same way, brought joy on a winter's day. As he left the Exchange hut, he waved to Squibs before hurrying in the direction of the town. But long before he was out of sight he stopped to greet and have a mardle with another regular 'signing on' client, Banker. Everyone in the town knew Banker, who was often described as a 'gentleman pauper.' In contrast to the little robin man, he was tall, upright and erect. He did wear an overcoat – a dark woollen one – with an astrakhan collar. The coat came well below his knees and on his head he wore a rollerway trilby that would have graced the Tattersals' enclosure at Newmarket! And this one had, until its former owner, old Colonel Laker, who lived in the Grange, presented it to Banker with the overcoat, in return for sweeping snow from his drive earlier in the year. Banker was always careful never to accept money in return for such duties.

"Clothes or wittles is all I ask in return, Sir."

When challenged by the Exchange staff, if they got wind of his activities, his stock reply was, "I did it out of the goodness of my heart."

Banker had found his own, rather crafty way of getting through the depression years of the 1930s. Who could blame him? He did little harm and this morning he did some good to young Squibs in his sick-bed.

Banker stopped to give the 'seel of the day' to the little robin man who told him about the boy looking from the sick-room window. Banker responded in his usual grandiloquent manner. He speedily completed his 'signing on' process, telling the clerk he had to help a 'poor young gentleman – out of the goodness of my heart'. He stood erect, looking up at the bedroom window.

Then he swept the trilby from his head in a pompous flourish and, raising the hat in the air at arm's length, he then bowed graciously, low to the ground. He arose majestically then called out, "Get better soon, young sir!" Then, much to Squibs' amusement, he and the little robin man staged a mock fight. Bearing in mind the size of Banker, and the handicap of his adversary, there ought to have been only one outcome to the conflict. But, somehow or another, Banker came off worse, sank to one knee, pleading for mercy. Little robin looked up to the window, grinning at Squibs. He removed Banker's trilby, placed it on his own head, putting his own old cap on to Banker. He arose, as if knighted. Then the two proceeded together, out of sight, up the road.

The day progressed; Squibs watched the various deliverymen calling, and the tradesmen from a builder's yard across the road leaving for work again after their dinner break. No lorries, but several builders' barrows left the yard. Wide and flat, they each had long 'T-ended' shafts for pushing and two large, spoked, wooden wheels. Each barrow was propelled by a tradesman, plumber, glazier, carpenter, joiner or bricklayer, with the tools of their trade aboard. A boy apprentice accompanied each one leaning on the pavement side of the barrow safely, lending a helping hand as they progressed up or down the road.

The railway station was only a couple of hundred yards away. The express steam trains to and from London stopped several times each day. The local station being the junction for the Lowestoft and Great Yarmouth line to Liverpool Street. Binner, the 'walking taxi', would be regularly seen passing up or down the road, to and from the station. Instead of hiring a motorised taxi, or carrying their own heavy luggage, many of the local shopkeepers, or gentry, who lived in walking distance of the railway station, used the services of Binner. Preceded by his customers who, unladen, walked quicker, Binner would amble up or down the road, a heavy suitcase in each hand.

His dress always the same – a navy peaked-cap (in deference to his 'walking taxi' title) and a long, faded-blue, gaberdine raincoat. Passed to him from some benefactor, the arms were too long and stretched over his hands, making the illusion that the burden of luggage over the years had stretched his upper limbs, which looked out of proportion to the rest of his physique. Because of his small stature, the cases he carried were only held an inch or two above the ground. He ambled slowly, his face never turning aside. He was blissfully unaware of Squibs, or anyone else. But he was always aware of those catching a train or arriving home from Liverpool Street. Binner was in regular demand and never had to call on the beneficence of the Labour Exchange.

The afternoon wore on, the February light soon faded. The boy dozed and his mum drew the curtains, lighting a small paraffin stove against the chilly night air. He sat up, only half awake, ready for his supper of pea soup, bread and butter with calves-foot jelly. "Erh!" he thought. The jelly was meaty in taste, not like the sweet lemon or pineapple jelly on Sunday for tea.

"It will do you good!" said Mum. Then he heard the cries of Smokes, the fish merchant. 'Merchant' was maybe too illustrious a title. Better to call him a 'Kipper Bloater Higgler'. Most days, Smokes would collect two large boxes of smoked fish off the train. These he would carry on long poles over his shoulder, to hawk in the street.

"Bloaters. Bloaters!" he cried. "Fine Kipper a pair."

But he also doubled as a Street singer. Not without a sense of humour in between each song, he cried, "Penny to go in the next street!"

Even if he sold no fish, he still collected a few coppers.

His voice made Squibs a fitting lullaby:

"Just a song at Twilight,
When the lights are low,
As the flickering shadows softly come and go."

Squibs 'Shuffs' Them Inter Colour

MR RIPLEY, the postman, who lived next door to Squibs, had fought in the trenches in the First World War. He had been 'mustard gassed' and had been left with a lifelong hacking cough and tired nerves.

"Neurasthenia, tha's what Dr Mac say that is," he told his friends, "The doctor say keep your mind occupied all you can but don't make yourself too tired."

A postman's job in those days was ideal for him. Regular steady exercise and the companionship of his fellow postmen. He moaned if it rained and blew hard, but said to himself, "It was better than the trenches." No hassle in those years leading up to and including the Second World War.

A keen gardener, he took great pride in his small front patch. It had a narrow circular crazy-paved path around a small centre feature. In pride of place stood the statuette of a girl. A picture of rustic innocence, she was placed on a tiny plinth, her hands coyly clasping her skirts as though to raise them from the plants growing around her. But she was not dressed for a garden and would have looked more at ease at a party or in the local juvenile dancing troupe.

As winter time got nearer and the nights started to 'pull in', Mr Ripley would gently lift her from her position of honour and wrapped in an old blanket she spent the worst weather in his 'shoe repairing shod' at the back of the cottage: "So she don't git a frawst on her."

Come next spring, adorned with a fresh coat of Snowcem, she emerged to grace the garden. When war came again, patriotic as ever, Mr Ripley replaced her with a slightly larger statuette of Field Marshall Lord Kitchener, in full military attire. He looked more at home gazing out across the garden. But Snowcem white did not seem quite in keeping for a valiant Field Marshall. Squibs' Mum was the first to point out to him the change one Wednesday evening when he left in uniform for the Wolf-Cubs' weekly meeting. Watching the lad depart from her bedroom window, she chuckled as he did a

He had been 'mustard gassed'

smart eyes-left and salute to the Field Marshall as he passed him on the pavement.

As the War progressed, Mr Ripley became busy with his spare time occupation as a boot and shoe repairer. This was his own cottage industry carried on in his 'shod', a substantial lean-to edifice at the rear of the cottage.

Mr Ripley had three daughters to care for and the extra income was a useful supplement to his postman's pay. The sedentary cobbler's trade was a suitable change from Royal Mail delivery. Several of his regular customers were fellow postmen and folks who lived nearby. An iron foundry producing munitions was close by and some of the workers, including a growing number of girls and ladies, would drop their boots and shoes off for repair as they passed.

He had one or two illustrious customers, notably Dr Mac and his wife – Mrs Mac. The postman's oldest daughter eventually worked in the doctor's household and there grew a strong bond between the two families. Dr Mac was justly held in high esteem by the whole town. The work of all the local doctors was valued, but Dr Mac was the people's doctor and loved by everyone. Not only was he a very good, kind and considerate GP but he was also a skilled surgeon. And he was good because he loved his work, which must have been endless. He took a surgery on Saturday evenings when his waiting room was overflowing. He too overflowed with confidence and humour as he attended his patients. No appointments were made. First come, first served, you took your turn as it came, summoned by a button-push bell, which the Doctor thumped to call the next patient. Often he did not finish his surgery until 9.30 in the evening.

One night when he had been busy all day and his customers seemed legion, he opened his door into the waiting room, calling out, "If you really must see me, wait – if you've come only for a chat and a bottle of coloured water, I'll see you next week." The room more than half emptied.

A year or so after the war, when Squibs was almost grown up, Dr Mac came to visit his Mum on an emergency call out. He gently examined her and quietly told her major surgery was required.

"I'll get you into the big hospital if you wish or I'll do it this afternoon at the cottage hospital."

Such was the confidence the family had in him there was no question what course to take. The job was soon successfully done and when Squibs' Mum returned home a few weeks later, Mrs Mac, a former nursing sister, arrived in the evening to provide night-time attendance for a few days. What wonderful loving care.

When he was ten-years-old, Squibs was allowed to sit in and watch Mr Ripley repairing shoes. Being wartime, the supply of leather was restricted, controlled and supplied by the 'Board of Trade'. Mr Ripley took the short train journey to Lowestoft and collected his allocation from a depot. The arrival of a fresh batch of leather was quite an event and Squibs was privy to the examination of the raw material to be used in shoe repairs. The leather was in quite large sheets about four feet square. Mr Ripley would examine it for quality and suppleness. Sometimes he would describe it as being "good and strong," suitable for working men's boots and shoes. Other samples were: "loverley, sorft and full of wear, just right to do ladies shoes." A twinkle would come in his eye as he commented: "keep a piece of that for Mrs Mac's shoes."

But once he was filled with despair at the quality of one sheet of leather.

"Look at this," he said in disgust, "Tha's neither tough nor supple – be as much good on your shoes as a bit of muck." He went on, "Smell it Squibs!" He had a nose for good leather. "Tha's just what that smell like – muck!"

On hearing the sound of the hammer, whenever he could Squibs would depart to Mr Ripley's 'shod'. He had a special viewing seat in the corner; it was an ideal spot for an hour or so on a wet day in the holidays or weekends. November was the busiest time for shoe repairs. The fog and wet soon exposed worn and leaky soles. Folks needed to be 'well shod' before winter ice and snow arrived. It was pleasant in the cobbler's den of an evening when the chill late autumn weather arrived. Mr Ripley's oil lamp supplied light and heat and the windows were blackened out and draught proof. The lad watched the complexities of a shoe repairer's work with interest.

A special type of rubber heel was designed to last longer in the wartime restrictions and it became popular with less sophisticated customers. The circular rubber heel was not shaped and fitted as usual but a special screw to the heel centre secured it. When the wearer had made it 'down at heel' the holding screw was loosened by the owner and it was turned and re-fixed until the whole rubber circle was worn.

Squibs liked most to watch Mr Ripley deftly cut a sole to fit a particular shoe, from the sheets of leather, and then the hammering process could begin. To facilitate the speed and ease of work he would place the nails required between his tightened lips. Thus, he could hammer the sole down without turning his gaze away from the job in hand.

"Don't you ever put nails in your mouth," he warned the boy.

After each pair of boots and shoes were finished, they were placed on a rack that stretched around the sides of the 'shod', awaiting the process of 'shuffing inter colour' – painting a liquid dye made up to match the shoe as near as possible. An artist's brush was used to apply the dye around the edge of the new sole. Before long Squibs was allowed to help Mr Ripley by doing this job on selected workingmen's boots. Eventually he became quite skilled and could pick the brush size and dye himself but awaited Mr Ripley's approval before commencing.

One November, with work at its peak, Squibs came of age. Mr Ripley passed a pair of Mrs Mac's elegant navy-blue court shoes to him, smiled and said, "You can shuff them inter colour."

Uncle Fred, Squibs and The Banished Duke

SQUIBS AND HIS BROTHER had lots of adventures during the war with Uncle Fred. Always there were rewards for helping in his 'Dig for Victory' campaign. Half the holiday time was spent in various jobs to help the home-grown war effort. On Saturday mornings Squibs helped the local dairyman and farmer on his town milk round. But early in the war he and his brother helped Uncle Fred do his large vegetable garden and his ever more productive allotment along the 'hidlands' of his friends' osier beds. These were down near the marshes alongside the Waveney River. The soil was rich, lush and fertile. Uncle Fred grew some of the 'masterest taters' you ever did see. He would not have spoken like that. He read lots of books, had quotes from Shakespeare for almost any occasion, came from Surrey and talked a bit posh. Once when he was in hospital the nurse wanted him to sit up and she needed some assistance from her patient, she said: "Mr Newton, will you please elevate your posterior?" He chuckled at this but did as requested asking: "Is that how you speak to all your patients?" "Oh no," the nurse replied, "I usually say 'lift yer bum, chum!"

One day, near the end of the harvest holidays, the boys had worked especially hard. Uncle Fred decided that he would provide a special treat, a trip on the river. Because of the war not much boating took place, but it was possible to hire a rowboat for the day. They set out for a Public House at Burgh St Peter on the River Waveney, the longest trip ever attempted. Each took a turn on the oars, but progress was slow. Realising there was quite a strong following wind, 'Frederick the Great' had another one of his inspired if somewhat bizarre ideas.

They had brought a large 'Gig' umbrella in the boat and if there had been a storm it would have given shelter to all three. Now, erected in the fore part of the boat, it acted like a spinnaker. With the wind gusting into the new-made sail, the boat glided through the rippling waters of the Waveney, reaching a speed no oarsman could have achieved. They passed bemused fisherman on both the

Norfolk and Suffolk banks of the Waveney. Any craft was the subject of interest but this particular one brought gasps of incredulity. Even a herd of young 'things' turned out on the marshland, ran to the riverbank and gazed in wonder.

Contrary to their earlier fears the crafty craft reached the haven of the riverside pub in good time for their dinnertime picnic. Full of self-aggrandisement at his nautical achievement, Uncle Fred ordered himself a pint and two lemonades for the boys. As a token to the theme that day he also got three hard 'ships' biscuits that sat in a large glass vessel on the bar. Captain and crew sat on the small pub jetty taking their refreshment and cooling their feet in the river.

The journey home was much more relaxed. As dusk came the wind dropped and with the tide in their favour, the little craft slowly drifted along. The boss took a turn on the oars, rowing in a leisurely manner. They watched the sun sink into the marshes. Bats replaced the dragonflies, zimming across the reeds. One great advantage of being on an adventure with Uncle Fred was that it did not matter what time they got home and Squibs was on the river later at night than ever before.

When the winter holidays came the adventures changed. But always Uncle Fred sought the joys of what he called the 'open air'. In January 1943, during the coldest winter of the war, a violent snowstorm hit the Waveney Valley and

Poor 'little ole fella' he sank deep into the snowdrift..

in places the drifts were surprisingly deep. Much of the flooded marshland was frozen and folk had started to skate over the sewer pans, always a risky business until the ice was safely thick. But now 'that wholly frooz hard'.

Uncle Fred suggested a walk to Barsham to look at the snowbound scene across the Waveney Valley. It was one of those clear crisp sunny mornings in winter that often follows a spell of wintry storms with heavy snowfall. The footpath they took out of the town was sheltered and eventually they climbed up a hill to look out across the frozen marshes. Here, no trees obscured the view. Because of this the snow had drifted to the top of the hedge. Frederick the Great called to warn young Squibs. Too late! The boy stepped deep into the drift. Poor 'little ole fella' he sank deep into the snowdrift and his rubber boots were filled with icy snow.

The excitement of this particular adventure was suddenly gone. Turning to his Uncle with a pathetic look of dismay, he pleaded, "Please, please, can we go home?" Uncle Fred, who was not usually a demonstrative man, clasped his arm around the boy's shoulder and stirred his body and heart with the words of the banished Duke in Shakespeare's *As You Like It*.

"Now, my co-mates and brothers in exile,
Hath not old custom made this life more sweet
Than that of painted pomp? Are not these woods
More free from peril than the envious court?
Here feel we not the penalty of Adam,
The seasons' difference; as the icy fang
And churlish chiding of the winter's wind,
Which when it bites and blows upon my body,
Even till I shrink with cold, I smile and say
'This is no flattery; these are counsellors
That feelingly persuade me what I am'.
Sweet are the uses of adversity;
Which, like the toad, ugly and venomous,
Wears yet a precious jewel in his head;
And this our life, exempt from public haunt,
Finds tongues in trees, books in the running brooks,
Sermons in stones, and good in everything.
I would not change it."

The words were to have a lasting effect on Squib's life!

Squibs, The War and Frederick The Great

BY 1940, the war had caused an influx into Beccles of various folks hoping rural Suffolk might prove a haven from the bombing in the cities. When Uncle Fred arrived with a carload from the Metropolis, the London Blitz had been raging a few weeks.

For all his high intelligence, or perhaps because of it, he was the worst car driver known. He had never come to terms with the use of a clutch. His car's Kangaroo-like progress down the road earned them the title of 'Uncle Fred and the bucking Talbot'. The day they arrived in town, Aunt Marge, one of his passengers, exclaimed as she inhaled the smoke of a Woodbine and downed a much-needed soothing cup of tea, "that journey was worse than the blitz!"

Uncle Fred had married Grandma's sister, a Suffolk girl, who had worked as a governess in Surrey, so he was correctly 'Great Uncle Fred'. The boys called him 'Frederick The Great', but not so's he heard them. His last name was Newton and because he was so wise and clever Squibs thought he must have been related to Sir Isaac.

An eccentric, he was full of a childlike enthusiasm for everything. But other things made him stand out in a small rural Suffolk community. He was a communist and an agnostic, but because of his kindly interest in everyone and what they were doing, the town somehow forgave him. He loved discussion and pitting his wits against ideas different from his own. He only chuckled when it was pointed out to him, "Communist you may be but you're the only property-owner in the family and the only one with a car."

He intrigued the boys. All their elders and betters were pillars of the Church and the Establishment. Not so Uncle Fred, who took the boys on what he called 'adventures' on a Sunday, which, until the war, were deemed unsuitable. War changed life in the town considerably. The cinema opened on Sunday evenings and even football matches were played in the afternoon. The aim was to provide entertainment and relaxation for the troops stationed in and around the town. A special football team was formed called Beccles

"Newton, come you down orf that there stack."

United. Drawn from the best players in local teams, who played their matches on a Saturday, they provided opposition for strong service teams. Likewise, in the summer local players and older school pupils played them at cricket. No longer was the Sabbath a boring routine of best Sunday-School clothes, church twice, jelly for tea and a sedate walk along St Mary's Road.

Aided by the war, Uncle Fred connived in the change and Squibs loved him for it. His Uncle played one of his trump cards – he was a great card player – and so enabled the lads to have an entertaining Sunday.

"They can help me 'Dig for Victory'," he told Dad, knowing his patriotic inclinations would bar any refusal for this break in custom. Uncle Fred's garden produced vegetables. Dad kept rabbits and poultry at home. Together he and Uncle Fred provided much home-produced food.

When he became a 'Fire-Watcher' in the Civil Defence, Uncle Fred's partner on patrol was another of the town's great characters. Mr Markwell, a basket-maker, living in the same road. When Uncle and Aunt had to move into 'rooms' he allowed him to grow vegetables on the 'hidlands' of his osier marshes, near the river.

Much to his and everyone's amusement, the fire-watching patrol covered the church and the Conservative Club. For all his left-wing leanings he always managed to quaff a pint of Tory ale when available, served by Squibs' Dad, who ran the bar in the absence of the steward, away in the army.

Life must have been unsettling for elderly folk who sought refuge from bomb-torn London. Aunt Jennie always made a 'home' in their several wartime dwellings. Possibly because their savings diminished as the war progressed, their abodes became more humble. Between moves they had spells at a farmhouse with card-playing friends. These stays were always short, but they both loved a spell in the country.

As usual, Great Uncle took an active interest in everything going on. One harvest, the men all sat in the lengthening shade near an almost-built corn stack, 'gitten their farses'. Uncle thought he'd climb up to the top and get a really good view of the surrounding countryside. Jimma, the stack builder, took great pride in his work and didn't want the likes of a 'Lunnener', as he called them, climbing all over his unfinished stack.

"Newton, Newton," he cried, "come you down orf that there stack. Blas', he's so brainy he's a bit sorft. I 'ont ha' you up there master," he said more politely as Uncle Fred rather sheepishly descended the ladder.

"That int safe for you. Do you have a drop o' cold tea and have a yarn. Thas what yah best at!"

Great Uncle Fred Back Pedals

GREAT UNCLE FRED had a passion for including cycle rides on his wartime holiday adventures. And this was one of the things still possible in wartime Suffolk. Cycling, even without the sensible helmets used today, was a safe and popular pastime. There was one proviso. When lighting-up time arrived, the blackout restrictions made it hazardous. Squibs was allowed as a twelve-year-old boy to ride anywhere in daylight. He rode his bike to and from school, on trips to the farm near the town to collect eggs and in search of hogweed for the family rabbits.

But come the harvest holidays a cycle ride with Great Uncle Fred was a popular treat. He cycled wherever he could on his antiquated yet well-preserved velocipede. It had a back-pedal brake rather than a fixed wheel. Pedalling backwards activated the brake and, until you got used to it, if applied too vigorously the cycle might be brought to an abrupt halt with disastrous consequences. Uncle Fred had mastered its use and he was certainly more expert on his bike than driving his car.

An ARP fire-watching friend was a skilful local basket-maker and he made him a deep basket to fit on the handlebars. On our expeditions it carried our picnic 'wittles' and pullovers and raincoats so we were able to withstand any hazards the day's cycling adventure might throw at us. The idea was that we would try and get lost. This was not too difficult, given that we proceeded along country lanes 'unsignposted' in wartime to confuse the Germans should they suddenly parachute on the scene. We often went into an area called the 'Saints', where even today folks sometimes find difficulty in reaching their destination.

'Lost' we may have been but always Frederick The Great would manage to find the village pub by lunch-time. He loved a half of mild and on hot days the other half, time us boys enjoyed a lemonade. The village pubs provided no meals and were quite happy for us to sit in their garden and 'git our wittles' which always included some of Aunt Jennie's rusks and a bit of

He cycled wherever he could on his antiquated velocipede.

cheese. Suffolk rusks were a good thing to take on a picnic. They did not get dry and spoil like bread would on a hot day.

Uncle Fred carried a compass and this was used to add to the excitement of finding our way back to the town. Squibs did once ask the landlord directions, who with a twinkle in his eye replied he was not able to give such information because of security. We might be spies for all he knew! This affronted the boy as he and his brother did not look like the Hitler Youth. They were loyal Cubs and Scouts. However, there was some cause for rural Suffolk to show concern about strangers as the county was full of airfields vulnerable to sabotage.

On these cycling escapades it was always a matter of principal and honour that they never rode back into town the same way they had left. A spider's web network of lanes, byways and tracks led in and out of the borough. Usually they were able to ride but if the track became overgrown and rough then to dismount and push valiantly only enhanced the excitement. Always there was something of interest.

An airfield was nearby and it was possible to get close enough to see planes landing. Many were dotted around a perimeter track, often just over the hedge. There were searchlight and 'ack-ack' batteries too. One way into the town was across a big area of common land. Troops and the local Home Guard used this for manoeuvres. These were better than any fireworks display. Thunder-flashes and smoke-bombs were hurtled around. Young Squibs had hated the idea of the war when it began but this all now seemed detached from reality. It was fun and interesting.

If they chanced to be on the Common at dinnertime, Uncle Fred found a secluded area near the marsh dikes. He taught the boys how to light a fire in a small pit. Dried bits of furze bush were ideal for this. They were allowed to burn out to a red-hot mass of embers. Into this were placed potatoes with an arrow of 'hoss-radish' root pushed into the centre. On very hot days they paddled in the marsh dike, which was fed from a nearby cooling 'pulk' – spring. Frederick The Great would stretch out on the grass, before carefully lifting his home-grown cooked potatoes from the fire. They toasted some cheese and enjoyed a wartime rustic banquet. The 'hoss-radish' gave the baked potato a tasty, piquant flavour. Nothing cooked at home tasted the same. They ate the meal with relish, like royalty at a banquet. No sophisticated barbecue, no theme parks, no holidays abroad. But the harvest holidays were idyllic.

Above: Garden in Belgrove Villas, 1931. *Above right: Belgrove Villas, 2003.*

Below: Uncle Fred's Talbot.

Above: In the garden at Belgrove Villas, 1931.

Below left: A family group in 1931.

Below right: Belgrove Villas, 2003.

An American Connection

YOUNG SQUIBS and his chums were growing up in the Waveney Valley. It was early in the last war and they had already formed a sort of American connection. 'Cowboys and Indians' was the favourite game in the back lane. Ken Maynard, a Western hero, appeared on the front page of a weekly comic, *The Tip-Top*.

On Saturday afternoons Hoppalong Cassidy and Gabby Hayes were heroes at three-penny Regal Cinema outings. They watched *Stage-Coach War, The Law of the Pampas* and *Santa Fe Marshall* to name but a few.

The Three Stooges comedy shorts, Walt Disney cartoons featuring Mickey Mouse and Pluto plus the feature film *Snow White and the Seven Dwarfs* enhanced the trans-atlantic flavour.

Then they began to notice girls. The shapely form and erotic charms of Betty Grable as the girl with the 'Million Dollar Legs' played a different, but no less significant, part. She was the star in a film with the unlikely title *The Day the Bookies Wept*. Poor Uncle Claud who had lost his beer money on the greyhounds, said; "I'll pay for us all to go and see the fillum. It will be worth it just to watch a bookie weep!"

Their vivid imaginations soon transformed the long back lane, where they played, into a prairie. A horde of Red Indians came charging across the nearby allotments to attack their 'covered wagon'. In reality this was the corporation dust cart pulled by Prince, the council Suffolk Punch. The boys followed it up the lane and its progress was suitably slow as the dustmen leisurely collected rubbish bins. Each galvanised, fully-laden bin was carried on the shoulder of the dustmen and tipped into the cart. Before the empty bin was returned it was dusted with disinfectant powder.

Mr Fairhead's pony-cart laden with logs and kindling became a stage-coach. He stopped for a few minutes and left skeps of wood at cottages in the row. But the American connection, though strong, was one of fantasy, film and make-believe. Then came the Japanese attack on the American fleet in

"They tell me they put peaches on their ham."

Pearl Harbour. The United States came into the war and changed the American connection. Fantasy became reality!

Stories concerning the GIs' prowess with some of the local girls were soon heard. Some young Squibs did not really understand. There was talk of Massachusetts' Knickers – one Yank and they were down!

But it was a true story about American Air Force girls when the lad first heard about the USA invasion into the Waveney Valley.

It was early evening one wet Monday with piles of damp washing in the kitchen. Anything to lighten the household gloom was welcome. Dad's story did this. He and his boss were on their way home from the Saints. This was an area near Bungay where folks, not native, easily took the wrong turning. The wartime lack of road signs added to the problem. At a minor crossroads a Studebaker lorry laden with American Air Force girls from a nearby airfield, anxious to savour the Bungay night-life, had lost its way.

"Can you please tell me the way for Bungay?" said the girl.

"Damn my buttons," his father told Mum at tea time, "you should have seen her. She leaned and grinned at us from the high lorry cab. Her skirts were above her knees. As she spoke they were hitched even higher revealing a most generous and gorgeous portion of American thigh."

"Betty Grable eat your heart out," I thought, "I'm glad the Yanks are in the war."

"Disgusting," Grandma puttered, "And they tell me they put peaches on their ham. You boys go and do your homework."

But as they did they tasted their first packet of American chewing gum which the girls had given father.

The real American connection had begun.

They tasted their first packet of American chewing gum

Neighbourly

WILLIAM AND DICK were neighbours. But never neighbourly. They ought to have had a lot in common. In their younger days, both had kept horses to pursue their living. But the changes that arrived when horsepower came more and more from an engine, affected them both in such different ways. A lot of the folks around thought, erroneously, that William might have been jealous of Dick, for he managed best of the two to adapt and flourish with the changes. Poor old William was no entrepreneur but found his own way of plodding along and this he was content to do. His disdain for Dick was summed up simply when he said to one of his pals, "I ont stand it when he run on all that squit."

Dick was a local yeoman farmer. He had arable and pasture land on either side of a small market town in Suffolk. Always a hard worker, he kept a productive and high-yielding dairy herd. The milk from this sustained a retail milk round, which he ran from his own home in the centre of the town. Here he had a dairy, which was run by his two equally hard-working nieces. Some customers had bottled milk – a recent innovation – but the bulk of the milk was served by hand at the doorstep, straight into the customer's jug. He numbered a lot of the town's population as his clients, from the high and the mighty, to the poor and destitute, living in the local lodging house.

"I 'int bothered who I sell to as long as they pay," he said.

Although they were not on good terms themselves, in the main William and Dick got on well with others in the locale, where they were both held in high regard and, in William's case, with affection. Dick did not seek this; when he was not working hard he was bent on enjoying himself. And this he did, by visits to the local greyhound and horseracing tracks. He was one of the few people in the town who made the long journey across the county to Newmarket when he always generously filled his car with some of his most-favoured dairy customers. Dick was too shrewd to gamble beyond his means but he loved a flutter and obtained what he called 'inside information', passing on tips to close friends. He also kept some excellent horses himself. There were three at the dairy premises. Kitty, a dapple-grey pony who provided spirited and graceful power for his milk float. Her mother, a more sedate grey mare, was stabled with her. She was on regular hire to the local woodman who delivered baskets of logs and kindling around the town. But his real pride was Jessie, a tall, bay, cross-bred hunter he used for elegant rides out to survey his farm on Sunday afternoons. Chance time Jessie was used on the milk round, as a showpiece at holiday times, or sometimes just to give Kitty a break.

'I have to work seven days a week' said Dick, 'but I like to give my pony a breather.'

When William was told this he disdainfully retorted, 'So he may, but the poor pony ha'ta pull him and the milk all round the town. He only scoop it into the women's jugs time he run on to 'em!'

Dick employed three backus boys; one was a young schoolboy who came after lessons each day to help for a couple of hours. On Saturdays, he went on the milk round to hold Kitty, time Dick collected the weekly dues. The other two backus boys were elderly men. Mr Neal did not come from a farm-working background. He was a gentle, old man who lived in retirement in a cottage nearby. A widower, he was glad to come and help, in return for company and the warmth of the harness house where he often sat applying saddle soap to leather. He was given a bit of cash, free milk and spuds. The third backus boy, Old Len, warranted a more exalted title. A retired horsebreaker and groom, his equine knowledge and experience was valuable, not only to Dick, but to others who sought his advice when buying or selling horses or treating their ailments. In common with most farmers in the area, Dick still used Shires on his farm but moved with the times enough to have one tractor and a lorry to cart the milk in churns to his dairy.

Len – now in the twilight of his career – loved to ease through the day around the yard. He schooled the lad in the grooming and care of the ponies. When day was done, he would sit with Mr Neal in the harness house, doing what he called 'polishin' the gear and mendin' the hoss collars'. With the other two he did his stint on the cross-cut saw, providing logs for indoors and their own stove in the harness house. They would pluck chickens, pheasants and partridges, bag up spuds or put apples in the store loft and generally were what Dick called 'being useful about the place'. They had no set hours but did their jobs at their own pace, helping each other as best they could. As winter came and the nights pulled in, their stove was lit, a tilley lamp pumped up and they would sit and mardle in the evening.

"That sef our home firen'," said Len. They suited their boss and he suited them.

Dick was held in high regard in the town, not only for his reliable and punctual delivery of milk but, also, for his disarming way with the lady customers. A bachelor – gay, he may have been but never lacked female companionship if he required it. He lightened many a sad woman's heart with his cheerful, saucy banter on the milk round. He knew his customers, never overstepped the mark and was able to gauge just how far he could go with each one. It was not surprising that the sound of Dick coming up the road brought a bit of sunshine into the sometimes dull, lonely, wartime life of many anxious housewives.

Neighbour William was a completely different character. He was older, short, stocky and stubborn! But he was tough and filleted out a good enough living to suit his own modest requirements. William was not without a twinkle in his eye at times but he was often heard to remark about Dick's banter, "He do run on, so he do! I'll only say something if that need a' sayin'."

But although they were not friends, they never argued. Over the years, there were one or two disputes over access and right-of-way, for they shared a common entrance to each of their properties down a short loke. William would never have a row. In the early days, if he felt things might become heated, he just walked away. Perhaps if they did have a proper row now and again it might have cleared the air a bit. Maybe they somehow enjoyed not getting on with each other. But their relationship festered more and more through the 1930s, and the middle of the war found them ignoring each other and not speaking. If communication had to be made between the two parties, for whatever reason, it was done through Dick's two nieces, who worked in the dairy. William got on fine with them.

The increased use of motor transport had a disastrous effect on William. For many years his main income had been from providing horse-drawn transport. He had two vehicles for regular hire, one a wagonette – which took parties of children and adults on treats, picnics and visits to fêtes and galas. For any event at the local Hall, he was hired to take children around the estate on joyrides. He also had a regular contract taking the local concert party to towns and villages in the area. But he also had a splendid and stylish horse-drawn carriage hearse and was engaged for burials by all the local undertakers. The two vehicles gave him a regular, and assured, source of

William allowed his flock to increase by letting some broody hens to set.

income for they complemented each other. In summer, the waggonette was needed during the long, warm, sunny days while customers for his other vehicle were plentiful during the hard frosts of winter. Alas, the coming of motorised vehicles put paid to William's transport enterprise. He told his friends, "I'll ha ta screw my loaf to get by and find another way to live."

For years before, he and his father had kept a cow for the house, plus a few old hens that ran around the nettus and scratched in his yard. The town fen and marshes were only about a quarter mile away. William, whose family had lived in the area for generations, managed to secure a long-term lease on a five acre piece of marsh and a small adjoining field of about a couple more acres which supplied hay. And so he became a wartime smallholder. His house cow was increased to a herd of five Shorthorn-cross heifers and one old Red Poll cow who stood out from her fellows, not just in colour and polled head, but also, by the size of her bag, which resembled an upturned Kremlin citadel. A large Rhode Island Red cockerel strutted proudly with the hens and William allowed his flock to increase by letting some broody hens to set. The ensuing pullets were good layers and the young cocks were raised and fattened, providing a useful addition to a, sometimes, scant wartime table. But in those days, no poultry provided eggs as the modern hybrid does today. Before the hours of daylight diminished, William preserved two galvanised buckets of eggs in isinglass, to cover the period when they were less plentiful.

William's day became one of blissful routine. In winter, the cows stood cosily in their small nettus overnight. Come summer, he collected them at dawn from the marsh. Their progress to and from the nettus was purposely slow and sedate. The lane to his marsh had a wide verge, which he allowed them to graze, while he walked slowly behind, leaning on his bicycle. He always chuckled to himself watching his cows having what he called 'a free feed from the Council'. It saved his own fodder and gave him, he said, a 'free gallon of milk each day'. So if they met anyone on the journey, he was happy to stop and have a chat. As they neared home, his yard dog, Gip, a Smithfield Welsh collie cross, ran ahead on William's command to see the herd turned into the loke leading to the nettus.

At milking time, William groomed the hind-quarters of each beast with a curry comb to remove the thickest mud before brushing them down. William sat beneath each cow in turn on a three-legged stool, which stood rigid on an uneven surface. But before this, each udder was washed in clean disinfectant and warm water. This was not only a hygienic precaution but also stimulated the cows to let their milk down. He was an adept hand-milker and soon had the milk level in his spotless pail rising with a froth thicker than any pint of Guinness at the local pub.

William survived through the war and was, to all appearances, quite content. Eventually, the war was over and by now he was an elderly man and no longer as active, confessing to his friends, "I int the man I was bor, I get the ole screws in my back and knees. That milking stool fare a long way down and harder to git orf than that used to – I reckon I shall ha'ta give the cows up."

Gradually his herd depleted and he did not replace them with young heifers any more. But although William slipped into retirement, he did not lack companionship. He was one of a small network of chums who walked into the town centre every Saturday and Sunday to listen to the Salvation Army band play. For a small market town, the band was excellent and much

The Salvation Army band and their open-air service.

appreciated in the parish. William was one of many in the local population who regularly came to hear the 'Sally Army'. He and his mates formed a small parliament of souls who gathered neath the lea of a covered alleyway, leading to the Falcon Inn which, in days agone, had a cockpit and, nearby, John Wesley had preached on one of his tours of the country. The parliament was a fascinating and loyal troop. One was Mick, a local window-cleaner who boasted that he drank seventeen bottles of Light Ale during one evening:

"Yet I shinned up my ladder next-ter-day. No problem."

He was reputed to be the best window-cleaner in the area because of a secret ingredient he put in his water bucket. What this was he told nobody but it was effective and his cleaned windows shone. Quick at his work he did the windows of the terraced houses in the town – front and back for 6d (2½p). Another fellow in the group was in a wheelchair pushed by a giant of a man who rejoiced in the nickname 'Gunboat'.

Leaning on the chair, and walking or standing beside, would be 'Hudge', a diminutive, little fellow of such small stature he only came up to Gunboat's waist. William joined this group regularly and they were happy to stand for an hour or so chatting and listening to the band. Such was the popularity of the Salvation Army Corps that there might, at times, be over a hundred souls around. But not all stayed as long as William and his cronies. William always wore his Sunday best. A blue serge suit with tight-fitting, drainpipe trousers. In winter he had a heavy, blue overcoat and, unless it was a blazing hot summer, a pair of highly polished, black buskins and never any footwear other than boots. He never owned a pair of shoes all his life. His head gear was a cloth cap like all the parliament wore, except the man in the wheelchair who wore a green trilby hat; "One of you others can fetch it if that blow away in the wind," he chaffed his mates. He was the most protected against the elements. A heavy woollen rug was across his knees and over this was a black oilskin covering, which he called his 'tilt'; it stretched over his legs and was fastened to special fittings on the chair, covering him to his armpits. In very bad weather another cape was draped across his shoulders. And if cold and frosty, a thoughtful landlady filled a hot water bottle, which lay over his knees. 'I can withstand anything the winter sling at me like this,' he laughed. The group chatted away together and one could be forgiven for thinking they took little notice of the Salvation Army band and their open-air service. But when the army Captain led prayers at the end of his testimony, they each reverently removed their caps in a token of respect. The service over the parliament took some refreshment at the Falcon. Mild beer in the warmer months but in wintertime, old ale was drunk. It wasn't heated but always served at room temperature. The band marched off to the citadel, their banner proudly leading the parade. On Sundays, when they marched by the parish church, they ceased playing so as not to disturb those gathered inside for Evensong. The only sound their footfalls and the regular muted thump on the big drum to keep in step.

Following, or walking beside, would be a posse of children, also trying to keep in step and enjoying the colourful devotions. But once beyond the Parish church boundaries, two quick thumps were made on the drum as a signal for the band to strike up again. By the time they passed the local cinema, now showing films on Sunday evenings, they had no concern in giving it the full blast of 'Onward Christian Soldiers'. No matter if cinema patrons had their attention to Bing Crosby's crooning interrupted by 'Like a Mighty Army Moves the Church of God'! Come to think of it, those most in earshot were couples on the back row double seats of the 'Little Luxury Theatre', as the picture house was called. And they were so engaged with each other they were oblivious to hymns, or crooners.

After one more tankard of old ale, from the Falcon taproom, the parliament would adjourn until next weekend. But they strolled along together saying goodnight to each other as they arrived at their separate dwellings. Gunboat and the others would first see the man in the wheelchair safely delivered into the care of his kindly landlady.

William and Gunboat were the last pair left. He had biked in from the country, leaving his cycle in William's nettus. Mounting his 'faithful steed', as he called it, as horses were still much in mind, he bade 'Fare thee well ole' partner', to his friend and carefully pedalled his way through the wintry blackout to his cottage, a mile or so out of the town. William would watch him to the end of his loke and call, "Mind how yer go bor," as Gunboat disappeared into the night.

There was always one weekend in summertime when the parliament's routine was completely changed. And this was in keeping with the majority of folks living in the parish and the environs, for those living in the surrounding villages were equally involved in all the town's events. On this occasion, it was the weekend of the Town Regatta, which always took place during the second week of August. Then the Salvation Army Band did not go straight to their citadel but continued past it and down to the river's quay, where they held a special service for all the locals, holidaymakers and boat crews arriving in town for the Regatta and Water Frolic.

Evensong over, it was the custom for church, chapel and mission-house goers, to all proceed to the quay, join in the service and view the armada of yachts, dinghies, cruisers and houseboats that had sailed up the River Waveney to take part in the Regatta. William, Gunboat and their small entourage joined the crowds following in the wake of the Army Band. The singing was hearty, notably so when everyone joined in the final hymn 'Eternal Father Strong to Save'. The perils of the Norfolk Broads might seem as nothing compared to those of a destroyer cutting through a storm-laden Atlantic. But the choice of hymn was appropriate, for at least two of the vessels moored at the quay had taken part in the gallant mission by little boats used in the rescue of the British troops from the beaches of Dunkirk a few years earlier.

The early post-war years have rolled by. It is now the mid 1950s. Dick has been able to retire into relative riches and prosperity. He had managed to sell some of his land on the outskirts of the town to developers, at an inflated price, enabling him to invest in shares in the growing frozen vegetable and fish trade. He sold the goodwill of his milk round to a larger dairy and, to the surprise of everyone, left East Anglia for the first time ever and went on a luxury world cruise. Upon his return, he visited his former young backus boy, now married with a family, taking them gifts from his trip abroad. He even offered to lend him money to buy a house at auction.

"My accountant will draw up terms," he said. "I will write a cheque out on the day of sale and you can borrow the money at 1% less interest than building societies charge."

Meanwhile, William was managing to scrape by somehow on his pension. He had no rent or mortgage to pay. Some of the land near his marsh was now used as allotments. When he strolled down there, the faithful old Gip by his side, he would often be given vegetables.

Two local fishermen, who had been his friends for years, were now retired but their sons now fishing would bring William a good feed when their trawler came in. In the main, William was content but worried about what the future might bring. How would he manage when he could not get about? Then, one winter in early February, William and Dick were both stricken by the Asian 'flu. It was the first time they had done anything together. Complications set in and both developed pleurisy and pneumonia. The two nieces became worried and agreed they were both 'good tidily queer. That int just a nasty tizzick this time'. The local doctor visited daily. William was treated as a panel patient. Dick paid privately. His doctor told him of a new drug called M & B, which would work like an antibiotic.

"It's rather expensive," he said but, persuaded by his nieces, Dick thought it best to give the pills a try. By the next week he was through the crisis and looked set to have a few more years on this earth.

"How's that other poor ole' fool?" he asked as the doctor watched him gingerly take his first steps around the bedroom. The doctor pondered, not wishing to betray patient confidentiality.

"This is a nasty bug you've both had; so many folks down with it. But I'll see if I can get the panel to sanction those M & B pills for him."

Dick paused a moment then pointed to a small pile of coins, ten shilling and pound notes on the bedside table.

"Take what you require from there doctor and get some – but don't say a word to him."

The doctor grinned – he knew there was not much love lost between his two patients.

"Thank you, thank you," he said and, as he collected the cash, added, "I'll call in now and see William."

So, thanks to Dick's generosity, he was also soon slowly on the mend.

A few weeks later, in early April, there was one of those clear, sunny, softly-aired mornings that gave a hint of the coming summer. All the errand boys were whistling as they went about their calls and the wives were banging the front doormats with joyous abandon. One of the nieces, arriving at the dairy, called in at William's as she passed to leave him a few rusks.

"Oh tha's a large morning," she exclaimed to him. "Make you think summer's on the way." Poor old William, still feeling the depressing effect of his illness and confinement, replied, "Yis – but we'll pay for it later. Tha's a weather breeder."

However, he took note of her words and an hour or so later, decided he would venture forth for a stroll down the loke. Dick, sitting at the window by the porch, felt the sun's warmth and decided he, also, would take his first stroll since their illness. And so they met face to face in the loke. Both looked each other in the eyes. You could have cut the silence. Then William broke the ice with the words, "We're still alive then!"

Dick replied; "Ah Bor – so we are."

They were neighbourly at last. Although it would be false to say they became bosom pals, for their outlook on life and their interests were so different. But from then on, they always spoke if they met. As one niece said to the other, "At least they do give each other the seel of the day now."

When Dick carved his Sunday roast he always cut a portion for William. They would never eat at the same table – but they shared the same joint!

The Clown and The Cleric

IT WAS 1955 when the clown and the cleric came to live in the road. Coming to the East Anglian market town from contrasting backgrounds, and for different reasons, their simultaneous arrival was pure coincidence. Apart from a polite 'good-day' if they passed in the road, it was to be years before they had any conversation. The parson had preached and ministered for years in a small country parish in the Waveney Valley. A great number of his parishioners were farm workers who, in most villages, made little contact with their clergyman, keeping their dealings with him as distant as possible. Accepting there had to be a parson in the village, they would tolerate him for occasions like weddings, christenings and funerals, when the local cleric matched, hatched and dispatched his flock.

There were a few occasions when the church congregation numbers increased, notably at the Harvest Festival, when rustic voices loudly joined in 'Ploughing the Fields and Scattering The Good Seed on the Land', but with thoughts on the Harvest Supper to follow during the week. The carol service – when mulled ale and mince pies might (with luck!) be served at the parsonage afterwards – was popular. But for the most part through the year, the local cleric was avoided and ignored. Children would be sent to his Sunday School and husbands were happy for wives to join the Mothers' Union and help at the summer fête and Christmas bazaar.

Farm workers saw the parson as someone who did not do a proper job. He did not have to rise early, except on Easter Sunday for early communion. His children would not attend the village school. His wife would have a maid - sometimes two – who lived in, did the housework and washing, much of the cooking and all the other menial chores. Small wonder that countrymen saw their parson in that light. They knew few parsons who would have lasted long pulling and topping sugar beet with rain running down their necks or endured a day feeding the drum when a steam engine and tackle arrived to thresh a stack of wheat.

In those days, every parish had its resident priest. Home visits were considered a portion of his calling. Spotted coming up the garden path by a rural worker, hoping for an evening of fireside ease after a day of toil in the fields, the comment was often made in dismay, "Blas' here come the bluddy ole parson. I'm a'goin ter feed the hins."

There were exceptions, of course; some families were said to have 'got religion' but they were mostly chapelites. One farm foreman was considered exalted enough to be invited to become 'people's warden'. He proudly told the men in his charge that, "I'm ter mow the chuch-yud an' go round on Sunday wi' the plaate."

For all this apparent lack of interest, every household took the Parish Magazine. Asked if they would like to see the parson and his church disappear, they would have looked at you amazed that such a thought would enter anyone's head. If they did confront the parson, they conferred on him the deference they presumed his station and calling demanded. But if they could avoid him, they did.

Occasionally, along would come a parson who did not fit into the normal mould. And our cleric, the Reverend Fox, was one. In his village before his retirement, if he was spotted by one of his parishioners coming up the cottage pathway to the door, his anticipated arrival called forth a request to "Put the kettle on mother, here come that dear ole parson. I'll just git half dozen eggs for his missus." And for 'his missus' to get half a dozen eggs, she must have been held in high regard.

Nobody minded her talking posh but, because she did not patronise people, she was fine. Mrs Fox would bake a batch of scones and rusks for the church bazaar herself. And when the women did the washing-up at the end of a function in the church hall, she would lend a hand. Even dear old Reverend Fox would pick up a cloth, something few of the village men would consider. Small wonder that when they arrived in the town, upon his retirement, they soon endeared themselves to their new neighbours and were the subject of much interest. A parson had never lived in the road before. Most of the homes were of modest pretentions, housing working men and their families. But by 1955, times were changing; there was a hint of post-war prosperity. Many were moving from smaller dwellings in the town centre to new, more spacious developments on the fringe. Some went into the larger council houses, a minority were even able to obtain a mortgage and buy their own home. Thus, a number of the town cottages became vacant. By now, many were being fitted with bathroom conversions or extensions. They were economical to heat, close to the shops and public transport – ideal for retired, elderly, gentle folk. One or two new bungalows were also being built on former tradesmen's premises, as they were also moving out of town; these were often occupied by retired schoolteachers or shopkeepers. The dear old parson and his wife would not feel out of place in their new abode. Their choice of dwelling was ideal as the cottage they had acquired was on the corner of the road. The windows looked out to the south and west and so their living rooms were light, gaining full benefit of any sunshine. The cold north and easterly aspects of their dwelling were sheltered by a thick hedge, as well as another cottage. The cleric's wife was younger than he and a handsome lady. The comment was often made, "Must be somethin' special 'bout the ole boy to get a wife like that."

They both loved gardening, reading and chatting to each other. Their cottage had a small plot, big enough for a couple of deckchairs in the summer. But only about two hundred yards away was a former small orchard and market garden, now let privately as allotments to suitable tenants. They had arranged to hire one and their plot had a huge Dr Harvey apple tree in the centre, beneath it a garden seat was placed. Most mornings, if the weather was reasonable, the Reverend Fox would be on his allotment. He planted rows of peas, beans, lettuces, beetroot and a row of early potatoes. There were six fellow allotment holders. Each had a separate plot but they often worked together. The younger ones helped the ancient gardeners with the heavy digging. In return, the older ones kept a hoe going along all the rows of vegetables during the week, to keep the weeds at bay.

Using the land next to the Rev Fox was a retired horseman who had worked a pair or Suffolk Punches, used as shunting horses at the town's railway sidings. He was a very skilled gardener and willing to share his knowledge and expertise. At mid-morning, he would sit 'neath the Dr Harvey's shade with Rev Fox and his wife, who by now had arrived on the scene bringing a large Thermos flask of coffee for them to share. The old horseman arranged for a load of muck to be tipped near the allotment gate. Together, they steadily barrowed it to their vegetable plots. They got both pleasure and produce from their successful vegetable growing.

Meanwhile, the clown had taken up residence in one of a pair of three-storied houses whose rear view overlooked the allotments. He must have very soon been aware of the Cleric but they shared no time together. The former clown was half Russian and half Italian and had performed in some of the great circuses around the world, starting with the Italian State Circus. Finally, he joined Bertram Mills at Olympia, in London, and then went on tour throughout the British Isles. Originally he was an acrobatic performer but, later, he suffered a fall sustaining a serious and chronic back injury. But the circus was in his blood and, through his determination, plus the loyalty and comradeship of fellow members in the troop when he eventually recovered, he schooled himself into becoming a clown. And thus continuing in the circus life he loved. But by 1955, Rossi – as he was known – had become well stricken in years, finding life harder and harder in the circus ring. He was offered a chance to retire. Another – younger - clown and his ladylove, a high wire performer, decided to purchase the three-storied house in the road. They wanted a base to come home to when the circus was not touring or if they were resting for a few weeks in winter. Rossi was allowed to live in the house rent free, in return for keeping an eye on the property. He always had it warm and stocked with provisions when the younger couple arrived. And so he arrived on the scene in the same year as Rev Fox and his wife. Neither wanted a life of complete leisure. The parson helped in local churches, as required, continuing to preach. He would often take a funeral service in the area, where his gentle and kind manner was welcomed.

You may wonder how a clown found work in a countryside market town. This presented no problem to Rossi, who soon found himself all the work he required. His constant companion was a little Jack Russell terrier, called Lucky. He referred to her as 'My Looky', teaching her to do various tricks, one of the most engaging being to leap into the crook of his arm on the command, 'Alleey Oop'. The trick was even more spectacular as the little dog had been taught to leap higher than Rossi's head, before falling safely into his arms. And Rossi's skill in the circus ring in the timing of each trick was especially noted in the 'Alleey Oop' routine. The cry 'Alleey' from Rossi was only the signal for Lucky to sit near his feet, her tail wagging furiously. Then, with her head cocked to one side, and her whole lively body trembling, she waited for the 'Oop' call before leaping high into her master's arms.

Most evenings the clown and his little friend would call at the Queen's Head Hotel in the town for his 'little toot a whiskey'. 'Looky' would perform some of her tricks for the customers who watched in surprised amusement, notably in summertime when the hotel was full of holidaymakers. Rossi would chat to them about his circus life and 'Looky' was soon earning her

They adored each other and were content to be together.

master extra 'toots a whiskey' and packets of biscuits for herself. News spread around the area of Rossi and his performing 'Looky' and they were soon engaged to appear at children's parties, fetes, bazaars and similar events. Then, Rossi would dress up in his original clown costume. He wore a bright multi-coloured shirt, baggy trousers with yellow checks, held up by wide, crimson braces. These he was able to pull out at arms length. But the most striking and clownish thing in his garb was a gigantic extended pair of shoes, which made his feet look enormous and out of proportion to the rest of his body. But Lucky was the star and children adored her. After many tricks came the finale, when the little dog would roll over and feign death. Rossi would pretend to be inconsolable. He shuffled close to his juvenile audience, activating a small appliance taped over the eyebrows. Mock tears trickled down the clown's face. And, in misery, he would cry out, "I'll have to fetch the poleese man!" On the word 'policeman', Lucky came back from the dead and, to the joyous yells of the children, scurried out of sight. But as Rossi took his final bow, his little friend reappeared in view and, after one more call to 'Alleey Oop', the little terrier made her highest leap of the night into the clown's arms. The pair then left to tumultuous applause. But all would not be over if the cheering continued. They would take yet another final bow and a few children would come on stage and be allowed to let Looky 'Alleey-Oop' into their arms.

Rossi never wanted cash for his efforts; he was concerned about the taxman. A bottle of whiskey was always useful but reward came in a variety of ways. Rossi, a frequent customer at the fish and chip shop, was often told, "No charge tonight, Rossi, there's six fish suppers paid for!"

Eventually, he had to move out of his free accommodation. His friends sold up, upon joining a continental circus. They got him a small caravan to live in and a local builder allowed him to site it in his yard, getting around the planning regulations by saying that Rossi was his night watchman and Lucky the guard dog! This was stretching reality way beyond the bounds of belief but nobody worried. At least, not initially.

Life jogged along for more than a decade for the cleric and the clown. Then, one morning, the dear old parson was found lying beneath the apple tree on his allotment, having suffered a stroke. Fortunately, his wife had just arrived with the morning coffee. An ambulance was quickly called and, after a few weeks in the local hospital, the Rev Fox was allowed home into the tender care of his wife. Alas, he would never garden again. Although his speech and reasoning returned, his body was paralysed down one side and he was to be wheelchair-bound for life. But his faith sustained him, coupled with the loving care of his wife. They adored each other and were content to be together, having time to chat.

Meanwhile, the clown also found his health was failing. For mobility, he now relied upon a small electric-driven carriage, supplied free to him by a circus performers' charity. Arthritis had set in on his old injuries. So, with his little dog on his lap, a pink ribbon tied around her neck, he sat in his carriage and they travelled together around the town. But the 'Alleey-Oop' days were over.

Then the passing years caught up with Lucky. She developed kidney trouble and had not even the strength to leap on to his lap in the carriage. It was obvious to Rossi that her joy in living had gone. And so, this time with real tears in his eyes, he took her to the local vet to, "Go quietly to sleep; no fetch a policeman this time, Lucky. It's the last thing I can do for you."

For weeks through the winter, he was very depressed and sought consolation in the 'little toot of whiskey'. Alone now, he found it harder to battle against the lifetime pain and discomfort his circus injuries had inflicted. But Rossi was not one to give in. He visited the Queen's Head and rode around the town into the sunshine when the weather improved.

On his way he had to pass the parson's home. The vicar would often be seated in his wheelchair on the pavement near their cottage. Rossi would stop his carriage for a few minutes and pass the time of day. Eventually, they started to have a regular, and longer, chat. The vicar's wife realised that this was doing her husband good and so encouraged the budding, if unlikely, friendship between the cleric and the clown. Rossi was soon joining the parson and his wife for coffee and, within a few months, took lunch with them every Thursday and Sunday. He, in his turn, repaid their hospitality by returning every Friday lunch with portions of fish and chips for his new found friends.

Fish and chips from a shop had never been a meal that had figured on the clerical menu. But Rossi extolled its virtues to them and, being brought up in the Roman Catholic faith, took pride in providing his new found Anglican friends with a fish meal on Fridays. He advised them he would get haddock and chips until the wheat came in ear and then plaice would be at its best. There were three fish and chip shops that Rossi visited, as in his clowning days all the owners had found him work. There would be a friendly competition for the parson and his wife to try and guess which shop their meal had come from. One had crinkle-cut chips. Another did not use newspaper as the final wrapping but dull, buff-coloured paper. The third still cut the chips on an antiquated machine and they were thick and uneven. Their fryer was still coal fired and the scent of the boiler – a bit like the old railway steam engines – seemed to permeate the newspaper wrappings. All three of these agreed that classy newspapers, like the *Telegraph* or *Times*, provided the best insulation to bring the fish and chip meal home in winter weather. The

Reverend's wife said that the wrappings made excellent firelighters the next morning, for her stove.

"All those years in a cold vicarage," she said, "and I never had the benefit of fish and chip paper to light the fire."

"But we didn't have a fish and chip shop in the village," replied the parson, rather sadly. He, too, had grown to love the weekly fish and chips and thought his Fridays might have benefitted earlier from such a treat.

Their friendship blossomed over the next year but the same could not be said of their health. One Sunday, they thought Rossi was very quiet and did not tuck into his meal with the usual gusto. Then, as they sat drinking coffee, he sadly announced that he would soon have to leave the town for he had been offered a place in a residential home in Surrey, for old circus performers.

"Oh no!" said the parson. But Rossi was emphatic. Although still, in name, a night watchman in his caravan, everyone knew this was not so. A resident recently retired into the town had complained to the authorities about the dilapidated old caravan she could see across the fence from her garden. A diffident council official had told him he could no longer stay there. The welfare officer had visited and had arranged for Rossi to go to the home in Surrey. And so, once again with tears welling in his eyes, he explained, "I shall have to go." But, in true show-business tradition, he tried to make light of the situation.

Their meal over, the parson's wife poured them all a generous glass of port. After replenishing their glasses, she said, "I think I've got an idea. We can get round this, I'm sure. My husband – please call him Donald – would miss you so much. And so would I. Why not move in with us? I'm sure the welfare people can arrange me some extra help to look after you both."

And so the clown moved in with the cleric. They ended their days together. When Mrs Fox was told she had acted in a saintly manner, she replied, "Not so. They are so happy together. They're good company for each other and easier to care for because of this. I'm no saint. I did it as much for my own good. I'd rather look after them together. Better to have a happy clown and cleric, than a sad old parson on his own."

And every Friday lunchtime, she walked into town to get 'Three pieces of fish and a shillings worth of chips'.

A Box of Sundries

HE WOULD HAVE been a wise man who had the forethought to buy every 'box of sundries' sold at auctions in the Waveney Valley during the 1940s.

Sorted, restored, cared for and safely kept, they would no doubt be worth a fortune now. Possibly someone did and is now a 'Sundry Millionaire'. It's even conceivable that all the bric-a-brac shops and stalls that occur in every town and market are the result of thoughtful buyers of a 'box of sundries' forty years' ago.

It always seemed to me a funny way to describe them. 'Sundries' was the term used by the Australian cricketers for extras. And you couldn't put a no-ball, a wide or leg-bye in a box and sell them! But of course the term 'sundry' is apt for both needs; 'items which need not be specified'!

October is the wild month of winds, hurrying clouds, acorns, berries and auctions. As a boy it really started at the end of September. The pain felt as the final days of the harvest holidays came was lifted by the fact the last Monday away from school coincided with the Michaelmas horse sale.

Alas, we returned to our desks on the Tuesday, the second sale day. But the Monday brought a boisterous and eventful conclusion to the vacation. No boxes of sundries at this particular and meritous sale. Every item needed to be well and truly specified. The catalogue always obtainable before the day of the sale showed entries.

'BEAUTY' – A six-year-old Suffolk mare. Sound; quiet in all gears. Stinted to 'BECCLES LORD FOCHE'.

He was a noble Suffolk Stallion; whose progeny worked hard on Waveney Valley Farms. But if the horse-sale was perhaps the great event of the year those smaller October farm and cottage sales were no less an attraction.

Alas, a sale could mean some family's tragedy. Sickness, financial failure or death. At best, and most often, it meant: 'Mr So and So gives up the farm on retirement'. At those tender years I was never troubled by concern at the cause of the sale. And by the way they rummaged and sorted through, commented on and laughed at the treasures of some family as they were hustled before the auctioneer, neither did many of my elders and so-called betters.

Ornaments: vases, pictures, photographs, china, samplers, all bundled in a seemingly-haphazard way into 'boxes of sundries'.

Perhaps for years a gilt-framed photograph of Aunt Maria had held pride of place on the mantelpiece beside a China beaker inscribed 'a gift from Llandudno', some relic of Uncle Percy's venture into Wales in 1926. Now after many years together they would be parted. Aunt Maria to some dealer's stand in the Portobello Road. Poor old Uncle Percy's souvenir from Llandudno looks for a buyer and a profit from a bygones' shop in a small

A box of sundries.

market town. But the memories it used to bring will be meaningless to the eventual buyer.

In my boyhood I was untouched by nostalgia at the sales. I remember standing, feeling a whisp of melancholy at the end of one small-holding sale. As usual there had been amusing events. A 'quantity of wire netting' came up for sale.

"Good as new," cried the auctioneer.

"Can't be," called a dealer, "it's full of holes."

Now the sale was over and I waited to be taken home sheltering in the doorway of an empty cattle box. A few minutes before I'd helped to drive six young things from this box across the yard into a cattle float.

They had stood knee deep in fresh golden straw all day. The thick straw bedding had been put down for them by their farmer owner on the day of the sale. Until the last, he took a pride in the care he gave his stock. As the cattle departed they left a trail of straw across the now muddy yard, churned up by the large amount of animals, people and traffic busying about the sale.

I stood in the doorway watching the rain wash the fragments of straw to be lost in the mud. To rot, and go forever, as one man's life's work had seemingly gone in a few hours of an auctioneer's shouting. But a life's work was not lost forever.

The land was left in good heart.

Fiddle Driller

WHAT MAKES memories? Why are some happenings, often seemingly of no great significance on the day, somehow embedded permanently in the mind? Why is there today this great interest in the past? Who knows? When I recount memories evoked from a few years I spent on a Norfolk farm in the Waveney Valley towards the end of, and during, the early post-war years, there seems to be an almost incredible interest.

What wonderful characters I met and worked with; what amusing incidents occurred. Certainly they must have some historical and sociological comment on rural life and attitudes of that time, but at the moment this is not my main concern. Those with whom I was privileged to work had a greater integrity and sense of purpose than any group I have encountered since.

Although some of my earlier attempts at the many and varied tasks on the farm caused amusement and good-hearted ridicule from my fellows, I certainly enjoyed myself. At the end of each day I also knew I had laboured. But one returns from the fields with a natural and happy fatigue, never felt at the end of more scholastic pursuits. We have a need to work with our hands, and possibly this feeling is at its best when close to the soil – communing with nature.

With hindsight I now realise how fortunate I was to have spent those few years on a farm which still kept a stable of working horses and a large herd of hand-milked cows.

To an extent the years have dimmed the memory of the actual order that events occurred. However, by their nature you can guess in what month, or at least the season, they took place. We would not have been lifting sugar-beet in May or fiddle-drilling small seeds in October. Fiddle-drilling I can well remember was the first job I helped with. It was the Easter holiday of 1945.

Fiddle-drilling small seeds – to many today, even rural folk, these words would mean little. A fiddle-drill – romantic. Fiddle – surely of the folk, and apt. It could not have been called a violin-drill, but a fiddle-drill is a fitting way to describe the means whereby the 'small seeds' mixture of grasses and clovers was scattered in a controlled broadcast by an agrarian soloist, playing

The Fiddle Driller.

his fiddle-drill across the field of slowly emerging barley, broadcasting the small seeds with an even and rhythmic beat. A pull on the fiddle-drill bow with each step of the sower, and here the skill came, allowing a slight variation to allow for a breeze.

My job was to help mix the small seeds. At the end of the week I was allowed by my new-found hero, the fiddle-driller, to just try and see how I would manage.

"Just you have a go, boy."

Alas, my broadcast – it wasn't. The seed fell in strips or clusters. I lost the timing of the pull-bow with each step. I had to hitch, to get in step like young boy scouts at an Armistice Day parade.

Although by now I was quite good at mixing the seeds on the barn floor, I was not able to master this seemingly simple job which this old man did with the ease of breathing.

So, to this first day I spent on the farm. A fine, clear, crisp spring morning. The pollarded willows that formed an avenue of dwarf-like trees across the marshland dam on my journey to the farm, were greening. The hedgerows, birds and wildlife of the countryside were awakening from winter slumbers. Spring had come late that year.

I arrived at the farm. It took me about half an hour to learn what a misnomer farm labourer was. Artist, technician, tradesman and devotee all in one. The holding and use of a shovel was a dance.

My instructor was old Ted, the eldest of three of the same family who worked on the farm. Father Ted, boy Bob, his first-born, and young 'Whoopee', the baby of the family who, like me, had been recruited as extra help in the school holidays. Holidays from school fitted in well with the farming year. Eastertime, of course, was mainly drilling. The fact that the long summer vacation was known as 'harvest holidays' is self-explanatory.

Each pile of seeds had to be mixed on the concrete floor of the barn, turned by shovel one way, back again and then a third time: 'Ter maake sure.' Old Ted placed me so that I could hold the shovel with my left hand holding the shaft and my right hand on the handle. The natural way for a right-handed person. The movement of turning was more or less automatic. I did not even notice that my workmate was holding his shovel in the opposite way. The problem came when we had to turn the pile of seeds back the other way. I quite naturally continued to hold my shovel in the same way, but this required me almost to turn around to keep the seeds turning in an even pile. Then I noticed the suspicion of a grin on Old Ted's ruddy face. What should I do? Try and bluster it out in my own way, or be brave enough to admit that I had to learn how to hold a shovel properly?

Fortunately, I had the presence of mind to allow Old Ted to show me.

Small seeds were scattered in a controlled broadcast.

"Do it like this," he said. "That'll fare to come gainer." By the end of the second day I had some idea of the method and rhythm, required. However, of even greater significance, I had acquired in Old Ted an ally and confidant who would aid me in the years I spent on the farm.

Each morning the various jobs were allocated by the farm foreman. We always stood in a group in the cart-shed near the barn, awaiting the orders for the day. Many a morning the start of each day was enhanced by Old Ted's: "I'll taake the Boy Squibs alonger me –."

Above: Farm sale in the Waveney Valley, 1980.

Below: A view from Boaters Hills, Gillingham.

Above: Hill Farm, Gillingham, 1937. Wedding of Grace Ashford to Sir Charles Collett.

Below: Margaret Ashford-Hull, son Michael and the author. Priory Farm, 2003.

Spring Quartet

DURING THE EASTER holidays of 1945, the chance came, on a farm in the Waveney Valley, for me to take part in a performance by a 'Spring Quartet'. Forgive the musical analogy, I was still a choir boy at the time.

Who were the members of this quartet? – the Smyth Suffolk Steerage drill. The steadiest and most reliable 'hoss' on the farm. Likewise the steadiest and most reliable man, And, finally, the 'treble' of the quartet – a boy. He was seldom steady, but hoped to be reliable.

Crops like sugar beet would require hand hoeing, singling and 'hoss' hoeing later in the growing season, and they had to be drilled with great accuracy. The drill had a fore-carriage with steerage wheels, beside which the driver walked, keeping the wheel in the wheel mark guide. Seldom was a pull on the plough line – a thin rope rein – required. The inflexible, plodding old mare responded enough by verbal commands, the degree of alteration in course achieved by tonal variation. A "wheesh" – right, "cuppa ha" – left. A gentle "whoo" always stopped her immediately; a muted mention of her name "Darlin" and she was off again.

Behind, following the drill, came the boy. Very necessary. In some ways he had the hardest job. I certainly thought so at the time. It was required that he busy himself behind the drill, watching to see the seed was feeding evenly down the 'coulter' tubes which ran from the seed box of the drill into the tilth.

What wonderful living seed-beds were prepared. Contrary to term, there was no slumber in those beds. The more comfortable the bed the sooner the seed sprang into life. But then life does emerge from bed events. Maybe seed-bed is a fitting term.

At the end of the field – on the headlands – the boy turned the seed supply off, then wound the coulters up to facilitate the turning of the drill. He had to help fill the drill seed-box from time to time from bags of seed previously deposited at strategic points along the headlands. I remember one aspect of this job. The unpleasant effect of the pungent dust of the seed 'dressing', a necessity of economic farming. An organo mercuric compound, it caused the eyes to smart and dried the throat.

"Spit it out boy," said the foreman. "Have a drop a' drink."

He spat skilfully and surreptitiously, his hand cupped across his mouth. He 'chowed' tobacco. Only a nicotine spray, I suppose! A big, ponderous man, with huge hands. I see him now, heavy green twill jacket on. It was London Transport, surplus to requirements. Originally destined for a Green Line bus driver, this one was to slowly pace the Norfolk fields rather than hurtle across the Home Counties. He would lean across the seed-box of the drill as we "let the 'oll mare git her wind". Not for him the flexible and supple movements of

The cat a' gotta kitten, the dawg a' gotta pup.

some of the jobs on the farm. But on the steerage drill, with the uncanny bond he had with the old mare, he was just right.

At first I thought he was morose; he was not an ideal tutor, and no doubt I was not an ideal pupil, but in time we built a rapport. His grey-green eyes often looked sad. But he was not really melancholic; he had nursed a sick wife for a long time and she had died not long before I came to the farm. He felt grief.

As the day progressed and more especially if the work went well, he would liven up quite a lot. Sometimes he sang. We even sang together.

"The cat a' gotta kitten,
The dawg a' gotta pup,
Pray old woman, is your rhubarb up."

He loved whist and phat drives, and went regularly, recounting to me during the day the events at previous ones. His 'baccy' was Churchmans Celebrated Counter Shag. Sometimes if his supply needed replenishing I would be despatched to the village shop.

"If you see the guv'nor on the way tell him you're going to the blacksmith's after a 'nut and bolt'."

The boss did on one occasion ask my destination. On being told he quipped, "He'll break his teeth on them bolts one day."

The foreman was really good at managing boys, and tempered his discipline with fairness. A literate man in some ways. He went 'round with the plate' in the village church. Constant regular hearing of lessons and epistles had given him quite a Biblical knowledge. He used to quote from the Bible if he wanted us boys to tackle one of the more unpleasant jobs. A cunning piece of psychology, many might think. He probably thought it to be plain common sense.

I remember one cold, wet morning when they required some kale to be cut, and marrow stem kale soaked you very quickly, no matter how well clad. He looked at my comrade, Whoopy, and me then, placing his hand on my shoulder, pronounced, "And Nathan said unto David, thou art the man."

I went without a murmur.

The Heat Wave

IT WAS THE HOTTEST part of the 1946 summer. The day before, we had been carting marsh hay. 'Round' hay we called it. Goodness knows why. But it served to differentiate from the top-quality hay grown on the upland part of the farm. Marsh hay was used as litter in the wintering yards for the young 'growing on' heifers, providing warm bedding plus a nibble.

It had been a torrid day on the marsh with not even a cooling breeze to ripple the ripening barley in the field which sloped down to the river valley. As we journeyed home, the loads securely roped, the cattle we passed seemed too hot even to graze. Clustered in a rough circle, within the shade of an oak tree growing in the 'loke' hedge, they stood nose to tail, each having the benefit of a neighbour's 'fly swish'.

Our drink bottles, normally lasting until 'fourses', were finished by noon. Replenished at dinner break with cool water from the dairy, in this sweltering heat the liquid soon became tepid.

Had we not experienced a heatwave this story would probably remain untold. It all started through a simple error. The boss purchased a young pedigree Berkshire at a special boar sale in Norwich which was destined to relieve the 'work' of an ageing Large White.

The breeding herd was kept at one farm, but as parturition approached the expectant mums went to the maternity unit at the other farm about one and a half miles along a minor road. A Saturday morning job was to leisurely walk a party of five or so of these sows to await the birth of their litters. The guvnor thought – he was a successful pig breeder – the gentle exercise did them good.

About half-way you were met by a 'boy' from the other farm bringing a similar bevy of 'dry sows' on their return journey to run with the boar again. At the meeting point, charges were exchanged, each boy thus ending up at his 'home' farm.

Alas, the lorry driver who carted the young boar from Norwich got the two farms muddled. So instead of finding the breeding unit he ended up at the maternity wing. No one was about the yards except one worker who,

"I've hooly murdered him!"

supposing the driver knew the correct destination, aided him in putting the boar in an empty loose box.

No great problem. Next morning a batch of dry sows was due to go to the other farm. It was thought the young Berkshire boar would be happy to walk with his ladies.

The journey started quite satisfactorily. The first hazard, a small one-gate level-crossing, was passed without mishap, the gate-keeper, as usual, standing on the open side to see the swine did not 'run up the line'. But his chance remark: 'Tha's a warmer ter day!' was augural. Most of the trip went well, but the boy eventually became somewhat impatient. Not without some justification, as on this particular day his instructions were to make the full journey. It was felt the boar would be bewildered if he met another batch of sows en route.

About half a mile from their destination the young drover became anxious to get there, and decided to 'stir the ol' beggers up a bit'. The boar was given a whack and told to 'git a move on'. This he certainly did. Unused to other than the most gentle treatment, in complete confusion, he hurriedly left the chosen path, hurtled across a ditch and with his 'wives' in hot pursuit blundered into a field of women picking blackcurrants.

With the boy following, but confused as to which way to turn them for the best, and accompanied by the cries of the startled blackcurrant-maidens, the boar and his sows charged up and down and across the rows of bushes at a speed which would have rivalled their 'Gardarene' forefathers.

Eventually, after some minutes chase and by now exhausted, they emerged through a gap in a hedge and wallowed into the cooling mud of a pond. Here the boy found them. Leaving them a few minutes to cool off he eventually waded in calling them out.

The sows with stifled grunts soon wallowed out, but alas, the Berkshire boar would move no more. His hoped-for days of connubial bliss were not to be. He lay dead in the pond.

Meanwhile the boss, who often rode around the farm on horseback, had been told by the blackcurrant pickers about the boy's escapades, although they knew not the final dire consequences.

He came across the boy a few minutes later, walking somewhat disconsolately away from the disaster. He stopped and looked down at the boy from his horse.

"They tell me you've been half murdering that poor old boar, sonny,' he said. Almost in tears, the boy paused and wondered how best to tell the 'master' what had happened, then suddenly he blurted out, "Half murdered him? – half murdered him? Go and look at the poor old begger in the hoss-pond – I've hooly murdered him!"

Stable Companions

"SHE'S STILL A HANDY old mare for odd jobs about the yards." So said Joe the hoss-man. He, the boss and the foreman were discussing which horses were to go to the Michaelmas sale at Beccles. It was the end of September, 1946, and this discussion was an annual event. Farm economics decreed that a horse not capable of pulling its weight in the farm work would have to be sold. But the old mare in question was something special. 'Aldeby Darlin' we called her, and a darlin she was.

Some people – too few, unfortunately – seem to bring out the best in others. They seem effortlessly to surround themselves with a feeling of tranquil happiness. The old mare did this. We all loved her. An everlasting memory I have was of the way she would turn and gaze at you as you walked into the stable. At the end of the day she would gently nuzzle you as you placed her 'bait' in the manger.

She was a lovely colour as well, a sort of chestnut flecked with black, although now the once dark hair around her eyes was greying. Grooming her was a real pleasure. I read recently that persons suffering from heart conditions derived benefit from having a pet dog or cat to coach. If this be so, then to groom Aldeby Darlin would be as good as a heart transplant.

Joe and the foreman could not be a part in sending this old mare to the horse sale and thence the knacker's yard. She had been the foreman's horse on the steerage drill for a decade. The bond between them was uncanny. The foreman was not a sentimental man but the gentle pat his massive hand gave her each time he pulled her bridle off betokened the affection he had for her. Sometimes when I had been following the drill with them and I felt like a rest, it was no use asking him for a break; but suggest the old mare needed to 'get her wind' and he would be sure to stop.

But now the old lady was past working on the drill, or other field jobs, and she was used around the farmstead carting small 'gig ups' of hay and straw into the yards. Soon she would be past even this. Joe and the foreman knew that the Michaelmas sale was the logical end for her.

They need not have worried. The boss loved old Aldeby Darlin more than

Smiler

any of us; she would not be sold. When I left the farm to go into the Royal Navy for National Service the old mare was still at the farm. Is there a heaven for animals? It would surely be hell without them.

We had another 'Darlin' at the farm – 'Gillingham Darlin'. A grey mare, also of quite a sweet nature. I often worked with her. She was the ideal horse for a boy. One of my jobs was to take her to Hoomy the blacksmith to be shod, usually a Saturday morning job. I would ride her bare-back with just a bridle on. I loved Hoomy's forge. He was everything a blacksmith ought to be; large and sinewy, stooped and a different colour from everyone else in the village. He was more the colour of a turnip, and as he worked over his forge the sweat would run in grimy rivulets down his brow.

The forge was dark and the almost lifeless fire would spring to a ruddy glow when bellowed. I would stand in wonder as he shaped the shoe on the anvil. Each heavy shaping blow of his hammer would be interspersed with lighter tip-tapping blows on the anvil itself, which gave the whole process a musical and rhythmic pattern.

When the job was done Hoomy would give me a leg up onto the mare again; only this time her new shoes would give a melodic ring as we started the first part of the journey home along the road.

"Mind she don't slip going down the hill," Hoomy would say.

I soon learnt the cry of 'hold up old mare hoss' if she did stumble.

We had another real character in the stable. 'Smiler' he was aptly called. Learned people say animals cannot smile. Fools – they ought to spend an evening with my Dalmatian bitch: she wrinkles her muzzle up so much with pleasure, sometimes it makes her sneeze. What is that, if not smiling? I defy anyone to tell me.

Smiler, the smallest horse in the stable, was a gay little fellow. Gay in the sense the word ought to mean. Bright, willing and with a tremendous zest for life. Always wanting to do more than his fair share of work. On his own he would pull a tumbril load of sugar-beet clogged down in a field, when other horses would have required a trace horse in front to help them out on to the road.

"Give him his head," the hossman would say. "No need to flog this willing horse."

I regret that we traded too much on his willing nature, allowing him to work too hard. But, and herein lies the charm of this little fellow: he did not believe in doing overtime. I suppose he felt, with every justification, that working as hard at he did, come 4 o'clock, enough was enough.

At 7 o'clock in the mornings he would walk unattended around the headland of a meadow while I threw out a load of sugar-beet tops for the cows. Attempt the same job in the late afternoon and you were obliged to use a different tack. You had to lead the little old hoss to that point of the meadow furthest from the gate. Then scrambling on to the load it was a mad rush to fling the tops off and hope to unload them before he reached the gate.

One evening we had been working a bit later than usual at one of the most distant parts of the farm, the journey to the stable being about two miles. Smiler as usual was becoming restless, so I thought I'd try an experiment as there were no roads to cross. I just said to him, "Go home then." His ears twitched in disbelief and he was off. Down the long lane he sped, with me walking behind. But gradually his quick walking pace became almost a trot. The call of the stable and his bait were too much for him. Fool that I was. Smiler certainly knew the way home well enough, but in his anxiety to be there he cut corners and a broken gate-post resulted.

"You'll be looking after the chaff and calder next time we thresh," said the foreman. Anyone who has done this dusty job will know my foolhardiness had not gone unpunished.

Nicknames

YOUNG SQUIBS HAD ALWAYS been interested in how people got nicknames. Dusty for a miller was obvious, others were harder to explain.

Dry Summer, Bean Eye and Wick Up were all born in 1921 in the same village in the Waveney Valley. Dry Summer arrived at harvest time when everywhere was parched and 'sere'. You can see how he got his name. Bean Eye came along several weeks later when they were 'troshin' beans on the farm. Curiously the little fellow had mottled eyes just the colour of tick beans. Wick Up, by a few months, was the oldest of the three babes. He entered the village scene one bitter January morning when 'that snew and blew a wind frawst'. Ole' Dolly Pargetter the midwife say, "Don't you let that babe git cowd. Do you'll lose him. He look as how he might not be a very good doer, so do you turn the wick up on the oil heater."

So they kept the babe warm, watched over him careful and called him Wick Up.

All three boys 'growed up' and went to the village school. Almost as a matter of course all three went to work with their Dads on the same farm. But the Second World War came in 1939 and Dry Summer and Bean Eye volunteered to go into the army. Luckily they both came through the war unscathed.

They come home 'arter the war' and both got married and settled down to raise a family. Dry Summer to an ATS girl he met at Aldershot. He was 'wholly proud' of her, he was. She was slim like a ballet dancer and just a bit sophisticated. Not 'bickety' so the village folks didn't take to her but just enough so Dry Summer felt she was special. She always asked for a small dry sherry in the pub. Bean Eye married his schoolgirl sweetheart. She'd gone as cook 'up at the hall.' She was a cuddly buxom 'mawther' who made lovely beef and apple puddins'.

But poor Wick Up, they wouldn't have him in the army. He grew up a little ole spindly chap who 'limped along good tidily' as he walked. But they thought a lot of him on the farm. He was consistent in rearing fine-looking calves and stock. He took such a pride in his work, caring for everything as though his own. His 'things' looked a treat when turned out to graze in the spring of the year.

Three land girls came to help him in the war. He really fell for the seductive Katie, but he was too 'frit' and shy to ask her to go with him to the pictures. In the warmth of a feather bed at night he hugged the bolster and dreamed that Katie was in his arms. Alas, at the time, the gorgeous Katie was doing more than dreaming in an American airman's arms.

The war finished, and farm life got back to normal. There were changes. Farms got bigger, the 'hosses' were gone, hedges were uprooted, the combine replaced the binder, and corn stacks no longer stood in the farmyard. A few years rolled by.

Bean Eye and Dry Summer had a family growing up. Wick Up, still single, lived for his cattle on the farm, his garden and a few ole hens, a pint in the pub and a game of darts. He was content, but not blissfully so. Secretly he envied his chums with a wife.

"You can't curl up with a dart board on a cold night," he thought.

One Saturday in the late 1950s, all three sat 'mardlin' in the pub about all sorts of things. Not surprisingly, the subject of 'wimmen' came up. By then they had all finished the second pint. Tongues were loosened. Bean Eye say to Wick Up, "Ha' you ever, like they say in the bible, 'known' a woman? That would be a wholly shame if you died a wonderin'. What about them land girls during the war when Dry Summer and me were away? Blas' bor you must a had plenty of chances then. They reckon that Katie was a bit of all right. That blinkin' Yank who set her sails was married all the time. He ditched her you know and got himself posted. Rotten blighter nearly broke her heart."

"Yis," say Dry Summer, "that kind ole parson at Haxfield took her in and give her a job at the vicarage. She still live there you know. The ole parson and his wife took a real interest in her child, treated him like their own."

Wick Up's face lit up with amazement. He had thought Katie had gone to America as a GI bride. Haxfield was only twenty-five mile away. He'd have a trip out there on his moped. Monday evening he collected a dozen of his 'ole hins eggs' cut a bunch of daffs from the garden and set off for his first bit of 'Spring Courtin'.'

Arriving at the vicarage he thought it best to go round the back. Moving across the garden, Wick Up's nerve failed him again. What if Katie had forgot him? That was fifteen years agone they worked together. He turned to retreat and a familiar voice called, "Is that you, Wick Up? Fancy seeing you again.

"No. Do you bring me a half-dozen on Mondays."

Would you like a cup o' tea? Come you on in bor. The reverend's away a few days and I'm all on my own. Are them daffs for me? How lovely, you allus was kind."

It was two hours before he left the vicarage. When he did he had a contented look on his face and a spring in his step. He say, "Katie that was the masterest cup o' tea I ever did have. Can I bring you a dozen eggs every week?"

Katie grinned and snuggled close to him.

"No. Do you bring me a half-dozen on Mondays and another half-dozen on Thursdays. Then you shall have a cup of tea like that twice a week. At the weekend we'll go to the pictures."

And so they did until Michaelmas. Then the ole parson married 'em!

Lots of Acorns, November 1946

"Lotta aackons 'bout ter year bor, reckon we're in for a hard winter." So spoke Mr Mackin the farm foreman to Squibs and Kit the landgirl.

'Gillum Darlin' (Gillingham Darling) one of the steadiest old mares on the farm pulled their tumbril beneath the acorn-laden branches of a massive oak tree. They were crossing a large area of 'parkland' where all the sows and gilts roamed. Many acorns were now falling, providing the pigs with an autumn treat.

Mr Mackin and his two assistants had mucked out 'Charlie Wag' the ole boar. The foreman had 'ringled' a couple of gilts so they did not root the parkland meadow. Then they had seen the drinking water tank in the yard where the sows slept was full. They put a 'jiggup' of straw down for them to snuggle in against the coming, cooler, autumn nights. The day's work was nearly over; they were happily making for the farmstead and stable a good half mile away.

'Steady, ole mare-hoss,' said Mr Mackin as they reached the park gates into the farm lane. Now even the sedate old mare quickened her pace a bit as she realised they were homeward bound. All were now riding. Mr Mackin on the old mare his heavily-booted feet resting on the tumbril shaft easing the burden of his weight. Kitty and Squibs sat together on the front ladder extension of the tumbril. There was no load for the horse to pull so it was quite in order to ride. But woe betide anyone who rode a horse pulling a heavy load.

All the workers on the farm were now making their way back to the farmstead. 'Brushy' the second horseman had been setting out muck heaps on an old wheat stubble and he too was crossing the parkland with a tumbril. A gang of six men who had been pulling sugar-beet now swelled the throng. Joe, the hoss-man had been working a pair of young colts in trace harness and was leading his weary charges to the comfort of the hoss-yard, stable and bait.

It was early November 1946 and had been a mellow, sunny day. Everyone enjoyed this time of the year on the farm. The rush and long hours of haysel and harvest were over, but the rigours of winter were yet to come. You could still find a warm and sheltered spot to rest come dinner time.

Squibs leapt from the tumbril to open the park gates. The youngest, he was expected to do such tasks. But the old mare had no intention of waiting for the boy to close the gates. Much to everyone's amusement the lad had to run and clamber over the tail-board of the cart. Kit held his hand and arm as she helped him aboard. He liked that, especially when she seemed in no hurry to let his arm go. Soon all the horses had reached the stable and were being unharnessed. Some of the younger lads with sweethearts to see that night left fairly quickly but many stayed yarning in the stable as Joe baited the horses.

Acorns were falling.

Nathan Turner, Margaret Ashford-Hull and David Woodward.

Squibs loved this time of the day listening to the older men yarning to each other about the day's events. He would help with the grooming of the horses before they were turned out into the yard always knee deep in thick straw. Then he'd collect his cycle from the cart-shed and join a flotilla of perhaps eight or ten men and girls journeying home. The foreman usually led this convoy setting a very sedate pace. Some of the men lived in the cottages on or near the farm and they soon said farewell with cries of; "Mind how you go bor." "Yis – cheerio ole partner." And the reply would come; "Don't be late in the mornin' – mind she don't lie on yar shirt!"

The foreman lived right down in the village street and was the last to say farewell to Squibs who lived across the river in Suffolk.

By now he had ridden round in a loop and could look back across the Waveney and marshes to the farm. But after a night of Suffolk slumber he would be journeying back across the marshes into Norfolk once again.

Squibs and the Christmas Post Round, 1946

THE BOSS LOOKED down from his riding 'hoss' and handed the boy Squibs his pay-packet. His custom was to ride round on his bay hunter handing out the weekly wages to everyone. It was an effective routine, taking him over the farm each week, keeping an eye on the crops and stock. He had a brief chat with the chaps as he rode across the fields from the 'home' farm in the next village.

Slightly eccentric, one of his unusual quirks was to pay wages on a Monday or Tuesday. He took a paternalistic interest in his staff and their families, thinking if the wives had the pay packet early in the week, the money needed for household requirements was plentiful. What was left over come the weekend was 'beer and baccy money'. But it was also convenient for the boss, who liked to visit local markets and corn halls on Wednesday, Friday and Saturday. He did the payslips and other farming accounts on a Monday. The wages were then ready to take around later that day or sometimes on Tuesday. He wanted the men to never be quite sure when he was liable to ride up on them. There were not so many stops for 'a droppa drink' if the boss was expected.

There was a workers code for letting everyone know the 'guvnor' was around.

"The ducks are about," Oily might say, as he pulled his tractor into the yard. Sometimes the signal might be a simple "Quack, Quack" from the postman calling at the farm if he spotted the bay hunter on the horizon as he came down the road.

Old Dolly pushed an antiquated pram around the lanes collecting tinder, blackberries and anything else she might usefully glean around the farm tracks. She gave the most tacit warning, for her call was just like a duck! This she did vociferously if the need arose. It was Dolly's call that alerted Squibs on this Tuesday in December that his Guvnor was near.

"Thank you sir," said Squibs accepting his pay. The plain, buff envelopes

"You wholly looked as if you were busy."

were carried in a finely-polished leather cylindrical case. It had long shoulder straps ideal for the rider to hold securely on hoss-back. Originally it had been made for his wife to hold her gas mask in during the war. Like so many similar objects, no longer required for their original use, it was now utilised in another way. Squibs used his Dad's former ARP warden's respirator bag, made of sturdy khaki canvas, to carry his 'wittles and cold tea'.

Cold tea was the farm workers' staple drink. Sweetened, but no milk added to go sour, the freshly-made tea was well strained into the bottle and thus did not 'stew'. The tea was kept in the shade or in very hot weather immersed in a dike or 'pulk' – spring water.

It was far from warm on this particular morning in early December. There was no frost but a biting wind blew from the north-east. It had been a hot dry summer. autumn had passed but the full rigours of winter had yet to arrive. The men told Squibs: "The cold wholly strengthen as the days slowly lengthen."

"Sonny," said the boss – he called all the boys Sonny, "how would you like a couple a weeks at the Post Office afore Christmas helping with the extra mail? Not much doing on the farm at the moment, don't need three boys. You live in the town, the other boys in the village. You can come back after Boxing Day. Have a go Sonny, I won't stand in your way."

Squibs spirits lifted. One of his father's confederates was related to the Postman Higher Grade who recruited the auxiliary staff. He'd get a job, he felt certain. There would be overtime at the Post Office and he'd be saved the long cycle ride to work on dark mornings.

"Thank you very much, sir," replied Squibs, "that will suit me fine."

The 'confederacy' worked well and he started on Royal Mail duties one Saturday in December with an extra day's work before the other auxiliaries arrived. He acted as 'boy' to the Head Postman, preparing for the extra work and staff coming. An added bonus was that his pay was more for work less physically demanding. Postmen walked a lot, that was no problem. He was still out in the weather but he could stroll to work and have all his meals at home. The cold tea bottle had a rest!

His first job was to put all the batteries in the extra torches required. Some of them still had the old blackout shields that directed the beam downwards. Squibs had to remove these. It was an easy sitting-down job after farm work. Although the so-called Christmas rush was coming there seemed to be an easy, relaxed air about proceedings. Later he had to help set up the temporary sorting frames. Those for letters and packets were placed in the schoolroom of an old Methodist Chapel. The parcel sorting was done in the local Baptist Chapel Hall. Services still took place here on Sundays and they had to be very quiet and circumspect when they worked on the Sunday before the Christmas Day Morning.

To this day one episode stands out vividly in Squibs' memory. At the height of the ‘rush’ the local newspaper sent a journalist and photographer to report on the Royal Mail and the loyal servants at work. Suffolk guile came to the fore. The outgoing London Mail was held back an hour or so until the journalist arrived. The parcel sorting frame bags were stuffed with empty mailbags. Then parcels were placed across the tops of the frame giving the impression the bags were laden with Christmas gifts. About ten ‘brace’ of pheasants and partridges, an address label tied around the neck, were hung down the side of the frames. A muster was made of staff that could be spared. All of the temporary postmen plus one lady. She was a frivolous middle-class woman who had enjoyed the ‘bonhomie’ and banter of the working-class through wartime munitions work. Counter staff donned ‘sorting’ overalls to swell the numbers in the festive photograph.

“You wholly looked as you were busy,” said the foreman when Squibs went back to the farm after Boxing Day.

“Yis,” he said proudly, “that needed a good tidy few of us to clear that lot. But we did it. That was a kinda Poost Orfice Harvest. We all had a glass a sherry Christmas mornin.”

'Owd Bob'

LOTS OF FOLKS worked on the farm when Squibs was a lad in the 1940s. It was a community able to fill a 36-seater 'charabanc' for various outings. They would go to the speedway on a Saturday evening and a load always went to the county show when all the men who could be spared had a days holiday without loss of pay. Soon after the war a trip was arranged to visit the *Palace of Varieties* at the Lowestoft Hippodrome.

If you counted the part-time help that assisted for harvest, threshing, blackcurrant picking and the labour-intensive growing of sugar-beet for seed the farm payroll was about thirty. A similar size farm today might be worked by two men, plus contract help. Squibs was not working on a typical farm maybe, but the staff level was not unusual for that time in East Anglia.

Farm labourers; what a stupid term to describe the boys, lasses, men, young and old, who worked the land. Call them labourers and you have a plausible reason to keep the wages low. Squibs' boss was one of the most benevolent in the region. But he relied on the several individual skills of his workers.

Squibs had a tumultuous time with Arthur the farm foreman. The boss had told him that the boy had come to 'larn farmin''. This was strange to Arthur. Boys were on the farm to be useful. If annoyed he would throw his cap on the ground in despair. Sometimes he could be disparaging and was wont to remark: "They call your father a finisher – you 'int even a good starter!"

But his better nature eventually came through and he'd ask the boys about the next Speedway meeting. He came on these trips and kept the scores for us in the programme, which he called the catalogue. The term stuck in Squibs' family. Even today, usherettes in the theatre look bemused when asked for a 'catalogue'.

Joe, the head 'hossman', was a keen racing-pigeon breeder and fancier. He won national fame with his birds. Another of his interests was linesman for the village football team. No referees assistant then! He told the two backs to play well up 'fo'ard': "I'll soon give the buggers off-side!"

Joe always topped up the corn-stacks when Squibs arrived at the farm. Arthur, the former stack-builder, felt unsteady atop the stack as he got older.

'Owd Bob' had become our 'hossman' emeritus.

Our 'hossman' Joe was very kindly to 'Owd Bob', a man renowned for his prowess as a 'hossman' and breaker in the parish and beyond. In his younger days he had walked a stallion to local farm mares. At the Michaelmas hoss sales at Beccles, 'Owd Bob' was one of the few men who skilfully braided the horses' tails and manes.

He lived near Joe and no doubt had passed useful tips to the younger man. Those old 'hoss-men' jealously guarded their skills and methods. Often their 'hoss-book' remedies were only passed on in families over generations. Joe knew he was lucky to benefit from 'Owd Bob's advice.

In time, due to changes in farming practice, the older man found himself out of regular work. Too old to be able to adapt to new farming methods, his prospects looked bleak. In his usual generous attitude the boss told 'Owd Bob' he could finish his working days on the farm.

He arrived one spring morning when the whole stable was being harnessed to leave. A full team had to be out that day. Two gangs of harrows, the Smyth steerage drill, an old mare in a tumbril to cart seed, and another for odd jobs about the yard, plus the tractor pulling a rib-roll. Joe was having a little problem with a young Shire filly recently put to work. 'Owd Bob's' presence soon calmed her. Then we all stood in the stable waiting for the head 'hossman' as usual to lead us out to the fields.

Joe paused a moment. Then he glanced at 'Owd Bob' with a look of respect and compassion on his face.

"I think you'd better lead 'em out, Bob" say Joe. The older man grinned with an almost toothless smile. He had only one muddy coloured molar left in the front. A useful anchor for his 'pipe 'a bacca'.

He straightened his bent form as erect as possible. No words passed his lips but he nodded to Joe. Gently he took the bridle of his 'hoss' and led us all out to work. 'Owd Bob' had become our 'hossman' emeritus.

The Author

DAVID WOODWARD

Born in Beccles in 1930, David was educated at the Sir John Leman School.

On leaving school he began work on a farm, followed by two years' National Service in the Fleet Air Arm.

He then studied at Writtle College of Agriculture, working in the agricultural field until 1968 when he became an unlikely civil servant.

Since his retirement, he has become a graduate of the Open University.

A champion of local culture and literature, David has written two books on Suffolk dialect and has lived in Frostenden, Suffolk, for over 20 years. He is married with one son and three grandchildren.

The Artist

MARY BROWN

Mary was born in Debenham, Suffolk, although she lived in London and Grundisburgh for a while before moving to Beccles where she attended the Sir John Leman School.

She studied art at Lowestoft College and Bath Academy, whilst her love of music encouraged her to study it as a main subject at Trent Park.

In 1954, Mary married a farmer and they had two children. Her knowledge of country life makes her an informed illustrator of this charming book.

Now retired from a lifetime of teaching she lives in East Anglia enjoying the company of her six grandchildren and the countryside.

Glossary

agone . . . . ago, days past

a good tidy few. . . a great number, most

back'us boy . . . . . lad who did all the odd jobs, many for the farmer's wife. Sometimes older men did this in semi-retirement

bait . . . . food for horses or cattle

bickety . . . . to have a high opinion of yourself and show it

bor . . . . used as a greeting in direct conversation between friends – bor is masculine

chance time . . . . . now and again

clung. . . . . dried up, shrunken

coach . . . . stroke or caress

copped . . . . gently thrown

fare . . . . seems, may you

festered. . . . . got worse, infected

flea pit . . . . local cinema

frawst . . . . frost

gainer . . . . the best way to do something

gay . . . . jolly, lively

gear. . . . . harness for horses

haysel . . . . time for haymaking

hidlands . . . . headlands, edges of field

hins. . . . . hens

honky donks. . . . . heavy hob-nailed boots

jiggup . . . . small load

large morning . . . a lovely, sunny morning

loke. . . . . track or lane

lunnener. . . . . Londoner

mardle . . . . gossip, yarn

masterest . . . . choicest, biggest and best

mawther. . . . . girl, young woman

nettus . . . . cow house

Shirley and David beside the River Waveney, 1956.

ole . . . . old

ole partner . . . . . . kindly greeting to a friend

'ont . . . . won't, will not

panel . . . . name given to local Friendly Society Club

pulk . . . . water spring

ringled . . . . putting ring in nose

screw my loaf . . . . be crafty, shrewd

screws . . . . pain in joints and limbs

seel . . . . time or season

sef . . . . saves

shud . . . . shed

shuffs . . . . shoves

shummaker . . . . . shoemaker

snew . . . . snowed

sorft . . . . soft, stupid

tatterlegs . . . . shortcakes

tilt . . . . tarpaulin, covering

titta-ma-torta . . . . see-saw

tizzick . . . . dry cough

weather breeder . . unexpected good weather thought to bring a bad spell later

well shod . . . . well shoed

whooly . . . . very

wittles . . . . food, victuals

young things . . . . . young cattle

yis . . . . yes

Local Titles
Published by John Nickalls Publications

A LEVEL COUNTRY

Sketches of its Fenland folk and history

A PHARMACIST'S TALE

The joys, delights and disappointments encountered preserving pharmacy history

CURIOUSITIES OF NORFOLK

A county guide to the unusual

GREAT OUSE COUNTRY

Sketches of its riverside folk and history from source to mouth

MELTON CONSTABLE, BRISTON & DISTRICT, BOOK ONE

A portrait in old picture postcards

MELTON CONSTABLE, BRISTON & DISTRICT, BOOK TWO

A further portrait in old picture postcards

NATURE TRAILS IN NORTHAMPTONSHIRE

NEWMARKET, TOWN AND TURF

A pictorial tour

NORTH NORFOLK

A portrait in old picture postcards

NORWICH – THEN AND NOW

A look at the city through old postcards and modern photographs

IN AND AROUND NORWICH – THEN AND NOW

A further look at Norwich and district

NORWICH – THEN AND NOW

A third selection of old picture postcards

ROBBER BARONS AND FIGHTING BISHOPS

The mediaeval chronicles of East Anglia

SHIRES, SALES AND PIGS

The story of an Ely family of Auctioneers.
George Comins, 1856–1997

SUFFOLK'S LIFEBOATS

A portrait in postcards and photographs

S'WONDERFUL

A symphony of musical memories

'SMARVELLOUS

More musical memories